SCHOLASTIC

100 MATHS ASSESSMENT LESSONS

TERMS AND CONDITIONS

IMPORTANT - PERMITTED USE AND WARNINGS - READ CAREFULLY BEFORE USING

Licence

YEAR 2

Scottish Primary 3

Minimum specification:

- PC or Mac with a CD-ROM drive and 512 Mb RAM (recommended)
- Windows 98SE or above/Mac OSX.4 or above
- Recommended minimum processor speed: 1 GHz

For all technical support queries, please phone Scholastic Customer Services on 0845 603 9091.

Caroline Clissold

CREDITS

Author
Caroline Clissold

Series Consultant
Ann Montague-Smith

Development Editor
Mary Nathan

Editor
Ruth Burns

Assistant Editors
Gemma Smith and Margaret Eaton

Series Designers
Joy Monkhouse, Micky Pledge and Melissa Leeke

Designer
Quadrum Publishing Solutions

Illustrations
Garry Davies, Baz Rowell/ Beehive Illustrations

CD-ROM development
CD-ROM developed in association with Vivid Interactive

Additional material
Transitional tests written by Joan Nield and Lesley Fletcher

ACKNOWLEDGEMENTS

Extracts from the Primary National Strategy's *Primary Framework for Mathematics* (2006) www.standards.dfes.gov.uk/primaryframework and the Interactive Teaching Programs originally developed for the National Numeracy Strategy © Crown copyright. Reproduced under the terms of the Click Use Licence.

Every effort has been made to trace copyright holders for the works reproduced in this book, and the publishers apologise for any inadvertent omissions.

Published by Scholastic Ltd
Villiers House
Clarendon Avenue
Leamington Spa
Warwickshire CV32 5PR

www.scholastic.co.uk

Designed using Adobe InDesign.

Printed by Bell and Bain Ltd, Glasgow

1 2 3 4 5 6 7 8 9   9 0 1 2 3 4 5 6 7 8

British Library Cataloguing-in-Publication Data
A catalogue record for this book is available from the British Library.

ISBN 978-1407-10184-2

Contents

100 Maths Assessment Lessons

About the series

100 Maths Assessment Lessons is designed to provide assessment opportunities for all children. Linked to the renewed *Primary Framework for Mathematics*, it also supports the implementation of the new *Assessing Pupil's Progress* (APP) guidelines by linking the new APP assessment focuses to the PNS Framework objectives. Each title in the series also provides single-level tests that can be used at the end of a year, or at any point throughout the year, to provide a summary of where, in relation to national standards, learners are at a given point in time. By using the titles in this series, a teacher or school can be sure that they are covering the mathematics curriculum and obtaining relevant data about their children's achievements.

Unit B3 ACTIVITY 2

Name Date

Problem solving

Answer these problems.
Remember:
- read the question
- find the information
- work out what to do
- check your answer

1. There are 80 sweets in a bag. 25 sweets are blue. 39 sweets are red. The rest are yellow. How many are yellow? 16

2. Max has £5. He buys 4 drinks for 50p each and a sandwich for £2.50. How much money does he have left? 50p

3. Susie had 65 plants. She planted as many as she could in equal rows of 10.
a) How many rows did she make? 6
b) How many plants were left over? 5

SCHOLASTIC PHOTOCOPIABLE

About assessment

100 Maths Assessment Lessons provides a wide range of opportunities for teachers and children to assess progress. There are three different types of assessment identified by the APP guidelines:

Day to day

Day-to-day assessment is an integral and essential part of effective learning and teaching. Teachers and children continually reflect on how learning is progressing, see where improvements can be made and identify the next steps to take. Strategies that should be part of everyday learning and teaching include:

- sharing and talking about learning objectives, learning outcomes and success criteria with children
- observing and listening to gather intelligence
- planning for group talk, peer assessment and self-assessment to help children develop as independent learners.

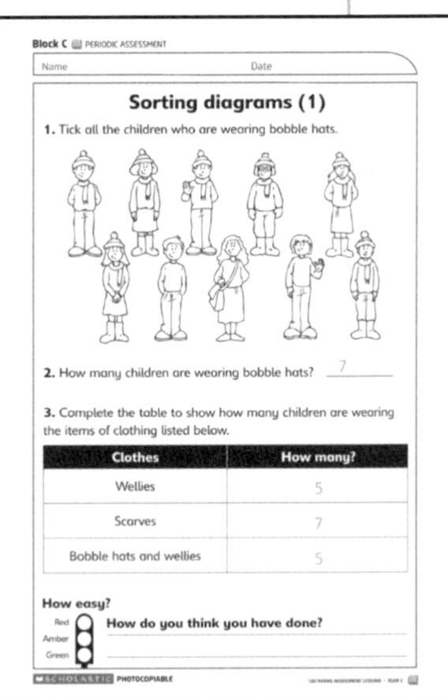

Block C PERIODIC ASSESSMENT

Name Date

Sorting diagrams (1)

1. Tick all the children who are wearing bobble hats.

2. How many children are wearing bobble hats? 7

3. Complete the table to show how many children are wearing the items of clothing listed below.

Clothes	How many?
Wellies	5
Scarves	7
Bobble hats and wellies	5

How easy? Red Amber Green How do you think you have done?

SCHOLASTIC PHOTOCOPIABLE

Periodic assessment

The purpose of periodic assessment is to give an overview of progress and provide diagnostic information about the progress of individual children, linked to national standards. It is intended to be used at regular (half-termly or termly) intervals to provide an overview of performance based on a wide range of evidence. Periodic assessment should be used to:

- make a periodic review of progress and attainment across a whole task
- identify gaps in experience and inform planning
- help learners know and recognise the standards they are aiming for
- involve both learner and teacher in reviewing and reflecting on evidence.

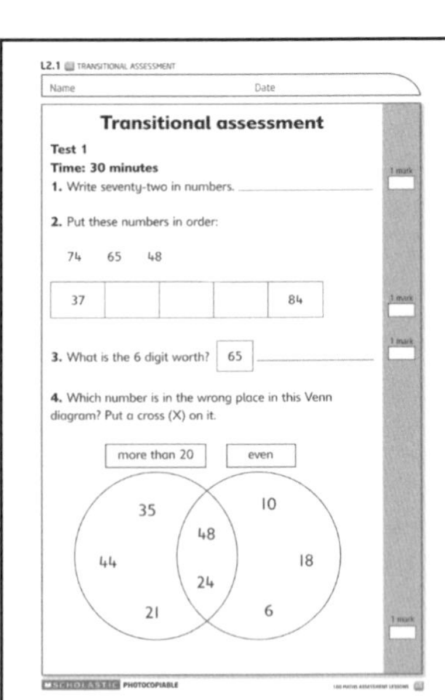

L2.1 TRANSITIONAL ASSESSMENT

Name Date

Transitional assessment

Test 1
Time: 30 minutes

1. Write seventy-two in numbers.

2. Put these numbers in order:

74 65 48

37				84

3. What is the 6 digit worth? 65

4. Which number is in the wrong place in this Venn diagram? Put a cross (X) on it.

SCHOLASTIC PHOTOCOPIABLE

Transitional assessment

Transitional assessment should be used at points of transition which might be from year to year, school to school or level to level. The pupils' progress data from day-to-day assessment and periodic assessment will support the teacher in making decisions about how pupils are likely to perform in transitional assessments. The key characteristics of transitional assessment are:

- it brings together evidence, including tests, to reach a view of attainment

- it is externally validated and externally communicated
- it is set within the framework of national standards.

For a complete list of strategies for day-to-day assessment and further information about periodic and transitional assessment, visit the National Strategies website (**http://nationalstrategies.standards.dcsf.gov.uk**).

About this book

This book is set out in the five blocks that form the renewed *Primary Framework for Mathematics*. Each block consists of three units, with each unit containing:

- an overview of the work covered in the unit, including the objectives, assessment focuses and learning outcomes for each activity (end-of-year objectives are denoted in bold text)
- day-to-day assessment activities based upon the assessment for learning and children's learning outcomes for each objective within a unit (note that the using and applying objectives are either incorporated into other assessments, or assessed on their own, depending upon the content and context of the unit)
- periodic assessment activities based on the end-of-year objectives within each unit.

Assessment activities

Each activity contains:

- details of children's expected prior learning before the activity is used
- the relevant objective(s) and vocabulary that children are expected to know
- description of the activity for the teacher or learning support assistant
- group, paired or individual work for the children. Where adult intervention is required, this is explained. Most of the activities include the use of an activity sheet or interactive activity from the CD-ROM
- clear differentiation, to support less confident learners in the group or to extend the learning for the more confident learners
- common misconceptions and how to remediate these
- probing questions to ask the children
- next steps: these are differentiated to help teachers decide how to help children who need further support. Suggestions for further work and references to related Framework units or blocks are given to support or extend the children.

What's on the CD-ROM?

Each CD-ROM contains a wealth of resources. These include:

- **worksheets** with answers, where appropriate, that can be toggled by clicking on the 'show' or 'hide' buttons at the bottom of the screen
- **transitional assessments:** year-appropriate single-level tests, oral tests, mark schemes and instructions
- **general resource sheets** (for example, number grids) designed to support a number of lessons
- **interactive activities:** for individuals or small groups, with in-built marking to assess specific objectives
- **Interactive Teaching Programs:** specific ITPs, originally developed for the National Numeracy Strategy
- **whiteboard tools:** a set of tools (including a pen, highlighter and eraser) that can be used to annotate activity sheets for whole-class lessons. These tools will work on any interactive whiteboard
- **display pages:** some activities require a problem or investigation to be shown to the whole class on an interactive whiteboard. The whiteboard tools can also be used with these images to annotate them as necessary
- **editable planning grids** (in Word format) are available to help teachers integrate the lessons into their planning.

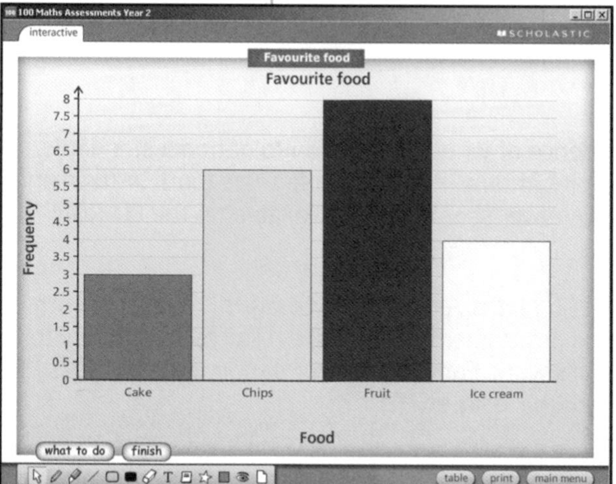

How to use the CD-ROM

System requirements

Minimum specification:

- PC or Mac with a CD-ROM drive and 512 Mb RAM (recommended)
- Windows 98SE or above/Mac OS X.4 or above
- Recommended minimum processor speed: 1 GHz

Getting started

The *100 Maths Assessment Lessons* CD-ROM should auto run when inserted into your CD drive. If it does not, browse to your CD drive to view the contents of the CD-ROM and click on the *100 Maths Assessment Lessons* icon.

From the start-up screen you will find four options: select **Credits** to view a list of acknowledgements. Click on **Register** to register the product in order to receive product updates and special offers. Click on **How to use this CD-ROM** to access support notes for using the CD-ROM. Finally, if you agree to the terms and conditions, select **Start** to move to the main menu.

For all technical support queries, contact Scholastic Customer Services help desk on 0845 6039091.

How to use the materials

The materials contained in the book and on the CD-ROM can be used with one child, a group, or in a whole-class activity. Decide who is ready to be assessed from the daily work that the children complete and from your observations. The CD-ROM allows users to search for resources by block, unit or lesson. Users can also search by Framework objective, assessment focus or by resource type (for example, worksheet, interactive resource, display page or ITP).

Day-to-day assessments

These should be used to support learning. They can be used during a lesson, when you judge that children are ready for an assessment activity. The materials can also be used weekly or after a unit of work has been completed.

Periodic assessments

These can be used with a group of children rather than with the whole class. This could be at the end of a unit of work (for example, at the end of a half-term or term). Decide who is ready to be assessed using the outcomes of the day-to-day assessment activities and your observations of children's performance.

Self-assessment

A self-assessment sheet is provided for you and the children to complete. It can be used where there is no activity sheet, so that there is evidence of the children's confidence in what they have learned and how well they can use that learning. There are 'traffic lights' at the bottom of the sheet that children can shade to show their confidence: red for 'need help'; orange for 'having some understanding'; green for 'go!' (ie the child feels confident with his/her learning).

All the activity sheets also have the traffic light system for the children to record their level of confidence, along with a space for them to write about how easy/hard they found the activity.

Transitional tests

These tests provide evidence of where, in relation to national standards, children are at a given point in time. Photocopiable tests (both written and oral), mark schemes and answer sheets are all available on the CD-ROM.

Class PET

A whole-school version of *100 Maths Assessment Lessons* is available with an expanded range of digital assessment activities, as well as the facility to report, record and track pupil's work. For further information visit the Class PET website, **www.scholastic.co.uk/classpet**.

BLOCK A

Counting, partitioning and calculating

Expected prior learning

Check that children can already:

- talk about how they solve problems, using the vocabulary of addition and subtraction and number sentences to describe and record their work
- count reliably at least 20 objects; estimate a number of objects that can be checked by counting
- read and write numerals from 0 to 20, and order these numbers on a number line
- say the number that is 1 more or less than any given number, and 10 more or less than a multiple of 10
- understand that addition can be done in any order and relate addition to counting
- understand subtraction as 'take away' and counting back, and find a difference by counting up
- recognise the value of coins.

Objectives overview

The text in this diagram identifies the focus of mathematics learning within the block.

Key aspects of learning

- Problem solving
- Communication
- Reasoning

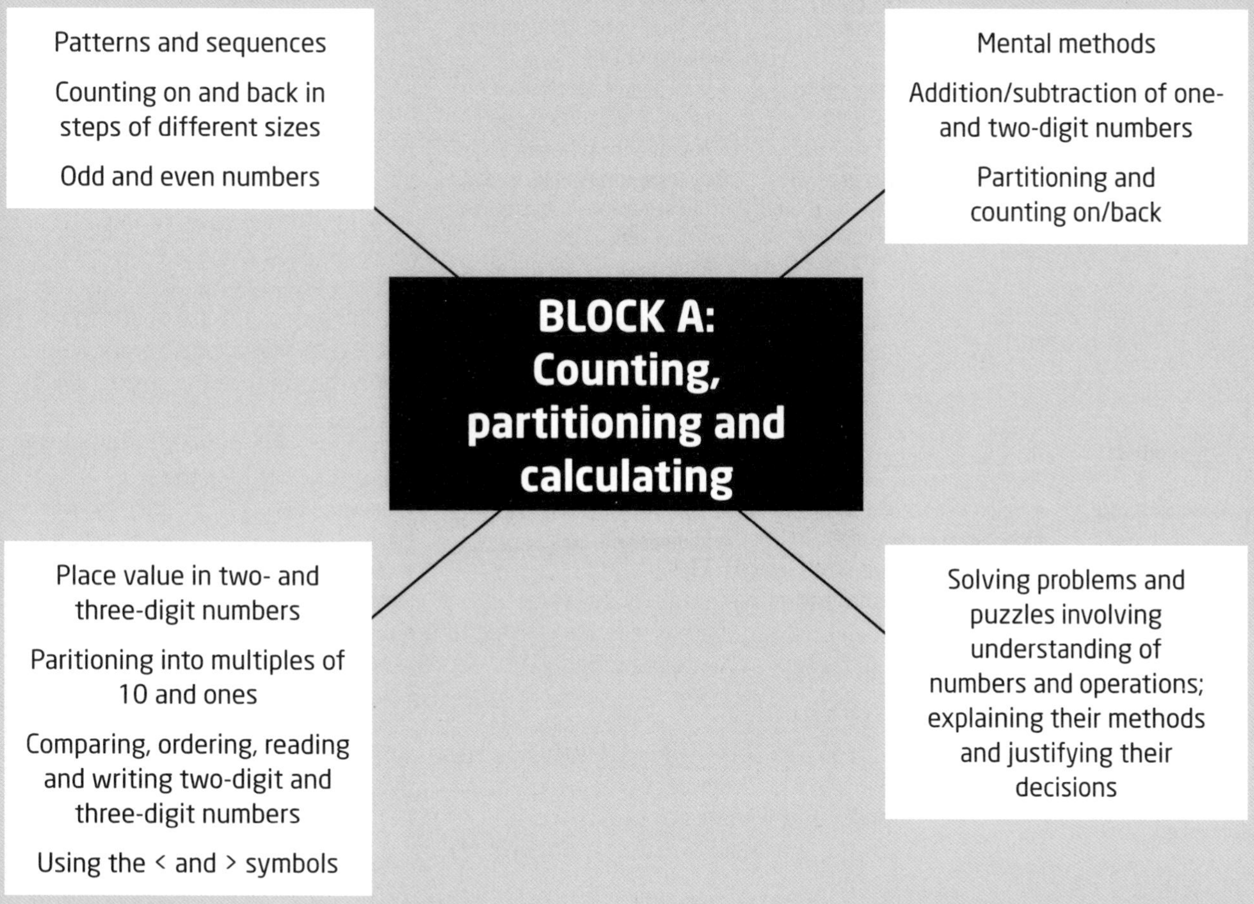

BLOCK A: Counting, partitioning and calculating

Patterns and sequences

Counting on and back in steps of different sizes

Odd and even numbers

Mental methods

Addition/subtraction of one- and two-digit numbers

Partitioning and counting on/back

Place value in two- and three-digit numbers

Paritioning into multiples of 10 and ones

Comparing, ordering, reading and writing two-digit and three-digit numbers

Using the < and > symbols

Solving problems and puzzles involving understanding of numbers and operations; explaining their methods and justifying their decisions

Unit 1 Counting, partitioning and calculating

Introduction

In this unit, children recognise patterns in numbers. They find the number that is 1 or 10 more or less than a given one. They count a large set of objects grouping them into twos, fives or tens. Children read, write and partition two-digit numbers. They order numbers, position them on number lines and compare sizes using the < and > symbols. They understand that subtraction and addition are inverse operations. They solve problems including those involving addition and subtraction of two-digit amounts using number lines and number grids. They explain their methods and results using mathematical language, jottings, pictures and symbols. Elements of explaining decisions, methods and results in pictorial, spoken or written form and using mathematical language and number sentences are encouraged in each lesson. At all times, the children should be encouraged to speak with clarity and respond constructively.

Framework objectives	Assessment focuses		Success criteria for Year 2	Learning outcomes
	Level 2	Level 1		
(1) Shopping				
Present solutions to puzzles and problems in an organised way; explain decisions, methods and results in pictorial, spoken or written form, using mathematical language and number sentences	• discuss their work using mathematical language, e.g. with support • describe the strategies and methods they use in their work • engage with others' explanations, compare... evaluate... • explain why an answer is correct, e.g. with support • test a statement such as, 'The number twelve ends with a 2 so 12 sweets can be shared equally between 2 children'	• discuss their work, e.g. with support • respond to questions and ideas from peers and adults • refer to the materials they have used and talk about what they have done, patterns they have noticed etc • draw simple conclusions from their work, e.g. with support • describe the different ways they have sorted objects, what is the same about objects in a set, how sets differ • identify which set has most items, which object is biggest, smallest, tallest etc	• can recognise all the coins to £2 • knows the value of coins to 50p • can explain how to solve a problem	*I can explain to others how I solved a problem.*
(2) Numbers				
Read and write two-digit and three-digit numbers in figures and words; describe and extend number sequences and recognise odd and even numbers	• begin to understand the place value of each digit • recognise sequences of numbers, including odd and even numbers	• read, write numbers to 10 • perhaps with some reversal	• can write the numbers to 50 • can order a set of random numbers • can recognise odd and even numbers	*I can read and write two-digit numbers.* *I know which numbers are odd and which are even.*

Unit 1 Counting, partitioning and calculating

Framework objectives	Assessment focuses		Success criteria for Year 2	Learning outcomes
	Level 2	Level 1		
(3) Count them!				
Count up to 100 objects by grouping them and counting in tens, fives or twos; explain what each digit in a two-digit number represents, including numbers where zero is a place holder; partition two-digit numbers in different ways, including into multiples of 10 and 1	• count sets of objects reliably, e.g. • group objects in tens, twos or fives to count them • begin to understand the place value of each digit, e.g. • use 0 as a place holder	• count up to 10 objects, e.g. • estimate and check a number • read, write numbers to 10 • perhaps with some reversal	• can count in one-to-one correspondence • can group objects into piles of 2, 5 and 10 • can partition two-digit numbers into tens and ones	*I can count objects by putting them into groups.* *I can partition numbers.*
(4) Ordering				
Order two-digit numbers and position them on a number line; use the greater than (>) and less than (<) signs	• begin to understand the place value of each digit; use this to order numbers up to 100, e.g. • know the relative size of numbers to 100 • use 0 as a place holder • demonstrate knowledge using a range of models/images	• order numbers to 10, e.g. • say what number comes next, is one more/less • count back to zero • place 1-10 into ascending order • point to first, second etc in a line • begin to count in twos	• can order a mixed set of two-digit numbers • can make two-digit numbers from single digits to given criteria • can position two-digit numbers on a number line	*I can write numbers in order and position them on a number line.* *I can use the greater than and less than symbols to show that one number is larger or smaller than another.*
(5) Rounding				
Estimate a number of objects; round two-digit numbers to the nearest 10	• begin to understand the place value of each digit, use this to order numbers up to 100, e.g. • know the relative size of numbers to 100 • use 0 as a place holder • demonstrate knowledge using a range of models/images	There is no assessment focus for this level	• can position a number on a number line and say which tens number it is closest to	*I can round numbers to the nearest 10.*

Unit 1 Counting, partitioning and calculating

Framework objectives	Assessment focuses: Level 2	Assessment focuses: Level 1	Success criteria for Year 2	Learning outcomes
6 Adding and subtracting				
Add or subtract mentally a one-digit number or a multiple of 10 to or from any two-digit number; use practical and informal written methods to add and subtract two-digit numbers	• use mental recall of addition and subtraction facts to 10, e.g. • use addition/subtraction facts to 10 and place value to add or subtract multiples of 10, e.g. know 3 + 7 = 10 and use place value to derive 30 + 70 = 100 • use mental calculation strategies to solve number problems including those involving money and measures, e.g. • recall doubles to 10 + 10 and other significant doubles e.g. double 50p is 100p or £1 • use knowledge of doubles to 10 + 10 to derive corresponding halves	• add and subtract numbers of objects to 10 • begin to add by counting on from the number of objects in the first set • begin to know some addition facts, e.g. • doubles of numbers to double 5	• understands addition as finding the total of two or more numbers • understands subtraction as taking away and finding the difference	*I can add and subtract some numbers in my head.*
7 Number sentences				
Understand that subtraction is the inverse of addition and vice versa; use this to derive and record related addition and subtraction number sentences	• use mental recall of addition and subtraction facts to 10, e.g. • use addition/subtraction facts to 10 and place value to add or subtract multiples of 10, e.g. know 3 + 7 = 10 and use place value to derive 30 + 70 = 100 • use mental calculation strategies to solve number problems including those involving money and measures, e.g. • recall doubles to 10 + 10 and other significant doubles, e.g. double 50p is 100p or £1 • use knowledge of doubles to 10 + 10 to derive corresponding halves	• add or subtract numbers of objects to 10 • begin to add by counting on from the number of objects in the first set • begin to know some addition facts, e.g. • doubles of numbers to double 5	• can add pairs of two-digit numbers • can use these pairs of numbers to make another addition and two subtractions	*I know that addition and subtraction 'undo' each other.* *I can write three other related number sentences for 6 + 3 = 9.*

Activity 1

Prior learning
Children can solve addition and subtraction puzzles. They can explain how they found their solution.

Framework objective
Present solutions to puzzles and problems in an organised way; explain decisions, methods and results in pictorial, spoken or written form, using mathematical language and number sentences

Vocabulary
pattern, sequence, continue, partition numbers, calculate, mental calculation, right, correct, wrong, number sentence, sign, operation

Resources
Interactive activity: Shopping
Resource sheets: Fruit cards, Self-assessment
Classroom resources: real or plastic coins

1 Shopping

Show the interactive activity 'Shopping'. Explain that you want to buy a teddy costing 60p. Ask the children to draw or write the coins that you could pay with. Encourage them to think of at least two ways. Invite them to use the interactive activity to demonstrate and explain their methods. Repeat with other amounts (multiples of 10p up to £1). Pose problems that involve addition or subtraction: *I am going to buy a 25p lollipop and a 55p bag of toffees. How much will I spend? What is my change from £1?* Decide whether to use the self-assessment sheet for children to record their achievements and what they need to do next.

Teacher support
Less confident learners: Provide the children with real coins to support their thinking.
More confident learners: Ask questions that involve prices that include amounts of pounds and pence to £5.

Common misconceptions
Children have difficulty knowing the value of coins.
Give children 29 pennies and ask them to count them out into groups of ten and exchange each group for a 10p coin. Encourage children to exchange any coins left over for 5p and 2p coins as appropriate.

Children think that the bigger the coin, the greater its value.
Give children one each of 1p, 2p, 5p, 10p coins and ask them to order them according to size. Place the equivalent number of pennies under each and ask them to tell you which is worth the most/least.

Probing questions
- How did you decide which information to use?
- How did you know which calculations to do?
- Could you draw something or use a number line to explain what you did?

Next steps
Support: To reinforce and consolidate, give the children fruit cards (cut out from resource sheet 'Fruit cards'). Ask them to match their prices with coins. See also Year 1 Block A Unit 2.
Extension: Give children a set of fruit cards. Ask them to work out the total cost of two or three items and find the smallest number of coins they could use to pay. Say they have £5 and ask them to find their change. See also Year 2 Block A Unit 2.

Activity 2

Prior learning
Children can read and write numerals from 0 to 20, and order these numbers on a number line.

Framework objective
Read and write two-digit and three-digit numbers in figures and words; describe and extend number sequences and recognise odd and even numbers

Vocabulary
zero, ten, twenty..., one hundred, two hundred..., one thousand, count in ones, twos, threes, fours, fives and so on, odd, even, pattern, sequence, continue, partition

Resources
Resource sheets: 0-9 digit cards, Place value arrow cards, Self-assessment
Classroom resources: plastic straws, whiteboards and pens

2 Numbers

Provide each child with a set of 0-9 digit cards. Ask them to make different two-digit numbers (for example, 34). They should read them aloud, and then write a number sentence on their whiteboards to show how the numbers are made up (for example, 34 = 30 + 4). Observe how the children do this and ask questions of the particular children you wish to assess: *Which is the largest number? How do you know? What is the value of that digit? Is this an odd or even number?* Then ask the children to write the numbers in words. Decide whether to use the self-assessment sheet for children to record their achievements and what the need to do next.

Teacher support
Less confident learners: Limit to numbers up to 30. Provide place value arrow cards so that the children can make the numbers and separate them to see the tens and ones.
More confident learners: Ask the children to make three-digit numbers and write the partitioning number sentences. For example: 264 = 200 + 60 + 4.

Common misconception
Children cannot write some digits correctly.
Provide children with large numbers to trace over and say out loud. Once they have done this, they could draw the numbers in sand or paint them on a large piece of paper.

Probing questions
- [Write 13 and 31]. Which number says 13? How do you know? What does the other one say?
- Is 567 even or odd? How do you know?

Next steps
Support: Let the children work with straws, as follows. Count out groups of ten and bundle them together. When you have several bundles, gather some and count in tens to find out how many straws they include and write the total. Repeat this, adding single straws to make different two-digit numbers. See also Year 1 Block A Unit 3.
Extension: Work on writing three-digit numbers with zero as the place holder for the tens number. Ensure that the children understand why the zero is necessary when there are no tens. See also Year 2 Block A Unit2.

Activity 3

Prior learning
Children can count at least 20 objects and estimate a number of objects. They can partition two-digit numbers into a multiple of ten and ones.

Framework objective
Count up to 100 objects by grouping them and counting in tens, fives or twos; explain what each digit in a two-digit number represents, including numbers where zero is a place holder; partition two-digit numbers in different ways, including into multiples of 10 and 1

Vocabulary
zero, ten, twenty..., one hundred, two hundred..., one thousand, count in ones, twos, threes, fours, fives and so on, odd, even, pattern, sequence, continue, partition

Resources
Resource sheets: Self-assessment, Place value arrow cards
Classroom resources: counters (up to 100 counters for each child)

3 Count them!

Work with a small group of children. Give each child a pile of up to 100 counters and ask them to count them. Observe how they do this. Do they group them in tens, fives and/or twos, or do they count them individually? If they count individually, interrupt them so they lose count, then ask them if there is a better way of counting them. Once they have counted them, ask them to write the number and then partition it (for example, 89 = 80 + 9) and tell you the value of each digit. Decide whether to use the self-assessment sheet for children to record their achievements and what the need to do next.

Teacher support
Less confident learners: Give children 30 counters to count. Observe what they do. If they count them individually, suggest that they group them in tens.
More confident learners: Encourage children to explore alternative ways of partitioning involving multiples of 5 – for example, 89: 85 + 4, 75 + 14, 65 + 24.

Common misconceptions
Children count a small group of objects, but have to count again if the objects are rearranged.
Arrange the same small number of objects in familiar and unfamiliar patterns and ask children to count each arrangement. Then ask them to rearrange them into other patterns and tell you how many there are.

Children cannot partition numbers into tens and ones.
Use place value arrow cards to demonstrate how to partition numbers. Give children their own cards so that they can follow your demonstration.

Probing questions
- Can you find a quicker way than counting in ones?
- Why is this better than counting in ones or twos?
- What makes 40 and 47 different?

Next steps
Support: Focus on counting and partitioning objects and numbers to 20. See also Year 1 Block A Unit 2.
Extension: Focus on exploring ways of making numbers to 100, linking with number pairs – for example, 89: 81 + 8, 71 + 18, 82 + 7, 72 + 17 and so on. Encourage children to look for patterns. See also Year 2 Block A Unit 2.

BLOCK A

Activity 4

Prior learning

Children can read and write numerals from 0 to 20 and order them on a number line or using place value. They can give one more or less of a number and 10 more or less than a multiple of 10.

Framework objective

Order two-digit numbers and position them on a number line; use the greater than (>) and less than (<) signs

Vocabulary

compare, order, larger, greater than, smaller, less than, between, half-way between, difference between, round, nearest ten, tens boundary, roughly, about the same as

Resources

Interactive activity: Ordering
Resource sheet: Self-assessment
Classroom resources: counters, number cards to 30, whiteboards and pens

4 Ordering

Write on the board: 27, 72, 34, 43, 18, 81. Ask the children to write the numbers in order on their whiteboards. Reveal the interactive activity 'Ordering'. Invite children to plot the numbers onto it using the pen tool. Write the greater than (>) and less than (<) symbols on the board. Invite children to choose two numbers and write them in the correct positions on either side of the signs. Decide whether to use the self-assessment sheet for children to record their achievements and what they need to do next.

Teacher support

Less confident learners: Ask these children to order number cards to 30. Write '<' and ask children to place cards either side. Repeat for '>'.
More confident learners: Extend the activity to three-digit numbers.

Common misconceptions

Children are not confident at ordering numbers.
Provide a number line to 20 and ask children to find 8 and 14. Use counters to work out which is the greatest amount.

Children are not confident using the greater than or less than signs.
Focus on one sign (for example, 'greater than'). Give children pairs of number cards. For each pair, ask children to say which is the greater number and then ask them to write a comparison of the numbers, using the 'greater than' sign.

Probing questions

- Which of these numbers lie between 40 and 50 on the number line?
- Which of these numbers could you use to make this statement correct? □ < 32
- Which of these numbers could you use to make this correct? □ > 51

Next steps

Support: Focus on placing numbers to 50 on a number line marked in tens. See also Year 1 Block A Unit 3.
Extension: Focus on placing mixed two- and three-digit numbers on a number line to 200. See also Year 2 Block A Unit 3.

Activity 5

Prior learning

Children can count at least 20 objects and estimate a number of objects. They can read and write numbers from 0 to 20, and position these numbers on a number track.

Framework objective

Estimate a number of objects; round two-digit numbers to the nearest 10

Vocabulary

estimate, roughly, about the same as, round, nearest ten

Resources

Interactive activity: Rounding
Worksheet: Rounding
Resource sheets: 0–100 numeral cards, Toy shop, 0–30 number lines
Classroom resources: counters, whiteboards and pens

5 Rounding

Open the interactive activity 'Rounding' and display the number line. Invite children to position different numbers on it. Talk about where each number goes, and whether it is closer to one 10 or another or halfway between them. Ask children to round each of the numbers placed on the number line to the nearest 10 and to write the numbers on their whiteboards. Provide the worksheet 'Rounding'. Talk through the instructions and ask the children to complete the worksheet.

Teacher support

Less confident learners: Work with numbers to 30 with these children. Provide the resource sheet '0–30 number lines' and counters. Ask the children to put a counter on 19 and then to tell you which tens number it is closest to. Repeat with other numbers to 30.
More confident learners: Work with numbers to 1000, rounding to the nearest 100.

Common misconceptions

Children have difficulty understanding rounding.
Give real-life examples showing why rounding is helpful (for example, estimating how much things are going to cost).

Children have difficulty rounding numbers.
Work in a visual way. Present children with a 0–10 number line. Put counters on different numbers and ask them to tell you which number is closest to 0 or 10.

Probing questions

- What is 26 rounded to the nearest 10? How do you know?
- I am thinking of a number. If I rounded it to the nearest 10, it would be 20. What could my number be?

Next steps

Support: Develop rounding skills for real-life purposes. Show the children the resource sheet 'Toy shop'. Ask them to choose a toy and round the price to the nearest £10. See also Year 1 Block A Unit 3.
Extension: Provide the children with the resource sheet 'Toy shop'. Ask them to choose two toys and work out their approximate total cost by rounding and totalling them. See also Year 2 Block A Unit 3.

Activity 6

Prior learning
Children relate counting on and back in ones and tens to their knowledge of one/ten more/less than a given two-digit number. They add and subtract ten to any two-digit number.

Framework objective
Add or subtract mentally a one-digit number or a multiple of 10 to or from any two-digit number; use practical and informal written methods to add and subtract two-digit numbers

Vocabulary
calculate, mental calculation, right, correct, wrong, number sentence, sign, operation, symbol, penny, pence, pound (£)

Resources
Display page: Adding and subtracting
Resource sheets: Self-assessment, 0-9 digit cards
Classroom resources: counting items, whiteboards and pens

6 Adding and subtracting

Reveal the display page 'Adding and subtracting'. Use the pen tool to write in additions and subtractions that involve a mixture of single-digit and two-digit numbers. For example: 7 + 5, 18 + 9, 50 - 30, 23 - 7, 21 + 12, 18 - 12. Ask the children to answer the calculations on their whiteboards and then invite those you particularly wish to observe to come and write the correct number in the correct space and explain how they found the answer. Decide whether to use the self-assessment sheet for children to record their achievements and what they need to do next.

Teacher support
Less confident learners: Concentrate on adding single-digit numbers to teens numbers. Give these children practical apparatus, such as counters or cubes.
More confident learners: Give these children calculations that involve adding or subtracting two sets of two-digit numbers. They could use jottings to help.

Common misconception
Children do not have reliable mental calculation strategies.
Focus on one strategy (for example, finding pairs that make 10). Provide calculations and demonstrate how the method works.

Probing questions
- What number facts can you use to help you work out 28 + 7?
- How might you partition 7 to help you?
- Is there another way to work this out?

Next steps
Support: Work with the children to add single digits to a two-digit number to 30, using the bridging-10 strategy. Write a two-digit number, provide counters for the units number, then take the required number of counters to make the number up to the next multiple of 10. Add the remaining counters. See also Year 1 Block A Unit 3.
Extension: Provide 0-9 digit cards. Ask the children to use them to make two pairs of two-digit numbers. They then choose a mental strategy to solve the calculation. See also Year 2 Block A Unit 2.

Activity 7

Prior learning
Children can solve additions and subtractions and understand that the order of numbers in a subtraction sentence does matter. They can record their answers in number sentences.

Framework objective
Understand that subtraction is the inverse of addition and vice versa; use this to derive and record related addition and subtraction number sentences

Vocabulary
addition, subtraction, inverse, calculate, mental calculation, right, correct, wrong, number sentence, sign, operation, symbol, penny, pence, pound (£)

Resources
Resource sheets: Self-assessment, 0-30 numeral cards
Classroom resources: whiteboards and pens

7 Number sentences

Write this number sentence on the board: 16 - 5 = 11. Ask the children to write three other number sentences from this without needing to do any calculations on their whiteboards (16 - 11 = 5, 11 + 5 = 16, 5 + 11 = 16). Provide 0–30 numeral cards. Ask the children to pick two cards and write the four related addition and subtraction number sentences. Observe how confidently they can do this and assess their understanding accordingly. Decide whether to use the self-assessment sheet for children to record their achievements and what they need to do next.

Teacher support
Less confident learners: Limit the number involved up to 10.
More confident learners: Use numbers to 100.

Common misconceptions
Children have difficulty making links between addition and subtraction.
Provide a number line and ask children to count on one, then back one. Make the link between adding and subtracting.

Children do not recognise that addition can be done in any order to give the same total.
Provide plenty of concrete experiences using such things as two piles of biscuits. Add the two piles together, starting with largest pile.

Probing questions
- If I know that 12 + 5 = 17, what else do I know?
- I had £20. I went shopping and ended up with £12. How much did I spend? How did you work that out?

Next steps
Support: Use a number line to count on and then back again to check answers. For example, for 12 + 8, find 12 and count on 8 to 20. See also Year 1 Block A Unit 3.
Extension: Provide money problems with amounts to £100. For example: *Mum gave me £60. I bought some trainers. I had £26 left. How much were the trainers?* See also Year 2 Block A Unit 3.

Unit 2 Counting, partitioning and calculating

Introduction

In this unit, children read and write two- and three-digit numbers with increasing confidence. They partition two-digit numbers in different ways. They count on from and back to any number in ones, including across tens and hundreds boundaries. They understand difference and find or describe the difference between two numbers practically. Using knowledge of number bonds to 10, they identify how much to add to any two-digit number to reach the next multiple of 10 and find sums and differences of multiples of 10. Children add or subtract multiples of 10. They use a 100-square or jottings on an empty number line to support their methods. The 'using and applying' objective threads are covered throughout all the lessons in this unit.

Framework objectives	Assessment focuses		Success criteria for Year 2	Learning outcomes
	Level 2	Level 1		
1 How many?				
Present solutions to puzzles and problems in an organised way; explain decisions, methods and results in pictorial, spoken or written form, using mathematical language and number sentences	• discuss their work using mathematical language, e.g. with support • describe the strategies and methods they use in their work • engage with others' explanations, compare... evaluate... • explain why an answer is correct, e.g. with support • test a statement such as 'The number 12 ends with a two, so 12 sweets can be shared equally between two children'	• discuss their work, e.g. with support • respond to questions and ideas from peers and adults • refer to the materials they have used and talk about what they have done, patterns they have noticed etc • draw simple conclusions from their work, e.g. with support • describe the different ways they have sorted objects, what is the same about objects in a set, how sets differ • identify which set has most, which object is biggest, smallest, tallest etc	• understands the term 'equally' • can share items into equal piles • can explain what they do	*I can explain how I solved a problem and say why I did it that way.*
2 Three-digit numbers				
Read and write two-digit and three-digit numbers in figures and words; describe and extend number sequences and recognise odd and even numbers	• recognise sequences of numbers, including odd and even numbers, e.g. • continue a sequence that increases or decreases in regular steps • recognise numbers from counting in tens or twos	• order numbers to 10, e.g. • say what number comes next, is one more/less • count back to zero • place 1-10 into ascending order • point to first, second etc in a line • begin to count in twos	• can read and write in figures any two-digit numbers • beginning to read and write three-digit numbers • can recognise odd and even numbers	*I can read and write numbers to 1000 in figures and words.* *I know which numbers are odd and which are even.*

Unit 2 Counting, partitioning and calculating

Framework objectives	Assessment focuses		Success criteria for Year 2	Learning outcomes
	Level 2	Level 1		
(3) Dominoes				
Count up to 100 objects by grouping them and counting in tens, fives or twos; explain what each digit in a two-digit number represents, including numbers where zero is a place holder; partition two-digit numbers in different ways, including into multiples of 10 and 1	• count sets of objects reliably, e.g. • group objects in tens, twos or fives to count them • begin to understand the place value of each digit, use this to order numbers up to 100, e.g. • know the relative size of numbers to 100 • use zero as a place holder • demonstrate knowledge using a range of models/images	• count up to 10 objects, e.g. • estimate and check a number • read, write numbers to 10 • perhaps with some reversal	• can group objects into piles of two, five or ten • can partition two-digit numbers into tens and ones in different ways	*I can explain what each digit in a two-digit number stands for.* *I can partition numbers in different ways.*
(4) Toy shop				
Add or subtract mentally a one-digit number or a multiple of 10 to or from any two-digit number; use practical and informal written methods to add and subtract two-digit numbers	• use mental recall of addition and subtraction facts to 10, e.g. • use addition/subtraction facts to 10 and place value to add or subtract multiples of 10, e.g. know 3 + 7 = 10 and use place value to derive 30 + 70 = 100 • use mental calculation strategies to solve number problems including those involving money and measures, e.g. • recall doubles to 10 + 10 and other significant doubles, e.g. double 50p is 100p or £1 • use knowledge of doubles to 10 + 10 to derive corresponding halves	• add and subtract numbers of objects to 10 • begin to add by counting on from the number of objects in the first set • begin to know some addition facts, e.g. • doubles of numbers to double 5	• can add two-digit and single-digit numbers mentally • can partition two-digit numbers to add or subtract • can explain other strategies for addition and subtraction	*I can add and subtract some numbers in my head.* *I can add and subtract bigger numbers using practical equipment or by writing notes to help me.*
(5) Symbols				
Use the symbols +, –, ×, ÷ and = to record and interpret number sentences involving all four operations; calculate the value of an unknown in a number sentence (e.g. □ ÷ 2 = 6, 30 - □ = 24)	• begin to represent their work using symbols and simple diagrams, e.g. with support • use pictures, diagrams and symbols to communicate their thinking • record their work in writing, e.g. • record their mental calculations as number sentences	• record their work, e.g. • begin to use the symbols + and = to record additions	• can recall number pairs to 10 • can recall pairs of multiples of 10 to 100	*I know how to write number sentences using the symbols +, –, ×, ÷ and =.* *I can explain what different number sentences mean.*

Activity 1

Prior learning
Children can solve word problems and explain their methods. They can solve number puzzles by choosing the correct operation (addition or subtraction) for the number sentences.

Framework objective
Present solutions to puzzles and problems in an organised way; explain decisions, methods and results in pictorial, spoken or written form, using mathematical language and number sentences

Vocabulary
pattern, sequence, continue, partition, calculate, mental calculation, right, correct, wrong, number sentence, sign, operation

Resources
Resource sheet: Self-assessment
Classroom resources: wrapped sweets, paper and pens

1 How many?

Assess groups of four children at a time. Provide plain paper for the children to record their thinking. Put 24 sweets on the table. *I want to share these sweets equally amongst you. How could you find out how many sweets each of you would have?* Watch how the children work this out on their paper. Do they draw representations of the sweets and group them? Do they share them out into four groups? Do they use their tables knowledge or count in fours? Ask them to explain what they did and why. Decide whether to use the self-assessment sheet for children to record their achievements and what they need to do next.

Teacher support
Less confident learners: Share ten sweets between two children. Let them do this practically.
More confident learners: Provide a higher number of sweets that will leave a remainder. Encourage the children to count in fours rather than draw representations.

Common misconception
Children do not understand the concept of 'equally'.
Use concrete apparatus such as counters and shapes, and place an even number of them into two equal groups. Repeat this several times until children understands that 'equally' means that there is the same number of objects in each of the two groups.

Probing questions
- What information did you use to solve the problem?
- Could you have solved it in a different way?
- How did you decide which calculation to do?

Next steps
Support: To reinforce and consolidate, give the children plenty of practice at sharing up to 20 sweets between two, four and five people. See also Year 2 Block A Unit 1.
Extension: Ask children more questions that involve remainders, without providing practical equipment. Encourage them to visualise and record in their own way. See also Year 2 Block A Unit 3.

Activity 2

Prior learning
Children can read and write two-digit numbers, and identify those that are odd and those that are even.

Framework objective
Read and write two-digit and three-digit numbers in figures and words; describe and extend number sequences and recognise odd and even numbers

Vocabulary
zero, ten, twenty..., one hundred, two hundred..., one thousand, count in ones, twos, threes, fours, fives and so on, odd, even, pattern, sequence, continue, partition

Resources
Interactive activity: Three-digit numbers
Resource sheets: Place value arrow cards, 0–100 numeral cards, Self-assessment
Classroom resources: whiteboards and pens, interlocking cubes

2 Three-digit numbers

Reveal the interactive activity 'Three-digit numbers'. Invite a child to make a three-digit number and to read it aloud. *Is the number odd or even? What does each digit stand for?* Ask the children to write the partition of the number (for example, 463 = 400 + 60 + 3). Invite a child to make their number sentence on the screen. Ask the children to make other three-digit numbers from the digits in the original number. Specify whether the numbers should be odd or even. Ask the children to pick one of their numbers and to make a sequence going up and back in hundreds. Decide whether to use the self-assessment sheet for children to record their achievements and what they need to do next.

Teacher support
Less confident learners: Work with numbers to 100. Provide place value arrow cards. The children make numbers and separate them to show the tens and ones.
More confident learners: Ask these children to make another number sequence that goes up and back in tens across hundreds boundaries, such as 377, 387, 397, 407.

Common misconception
Children cannot distinguish between odd and even numbers.
Ask children to make towers of 1, 2, 3... 9, 10 interlocking cubes. Which towers can be broken in half to make two towers that are the same height? Explain that an even number can be divided equally into halves and an odd number can't. Demonstrate identifying whether a number is odd or even by looking at the last digit.

Probing questions
- What numbers can you make using these digits?
- Is this number odd or even? How do you know?

Next steps
Support: Give the children some two-digit number cards and ask them to place them in two piles, one for odd numbers, the other for even. Next, ask them to make some of these numbers, using place value arrow cards and to write number sentences. See also Year 2 Block A Unit 1.
Extension: Ask children to make four-digit numbers and to read and partition them. Ensure they place zero in the tens and hundreds positions in some of them to reinforce its purpose as a place holder. See also Year 2 Block A Unit 3.

Activity 3

Prior learning

Children can count up to 100 objects, grouping them into twos, fives or tens, recognising that this is more efficient than counting in ones. They can explain what each digit in a two-digit number represents and the differences between their values.

Framework objective

Count up to 100 objects by grouping them and counting in tens, fives or twos; explain what each digit in a two-digit number represents, including numbers where zero is a place holder; partition two-digit numbers in different ways, including into multiples of 10 and 1

Vocabulary

zero, ten, twenty..., one hundred, two hundred..., one thousand, count in ones, twos, threes, fours, fives and so on, odd, even, pattern, sequence, continue, partition

Resources

Interactive activity: Dominoes
Classroom resources: dominoes, counting objects, place value equipment

3 Dominoes

Reveal the interactive activity 'Dominoes'. Move five dominoes into the working area and ask the children to estimate the total number of spots. Ask them to look for individual or pairs of dominoes that total 10, and group them together. Then circle those totalling 5 and 2. Count the tens, then count on the fives, twos and finally the others. *Compare the total with your estimate.* Ask children to partition the total (for example, 57: 50 + 7, 40 + 17, 30 + 27) and to tell you the value of each digit. Repeat the activity with a different set of dominoes.

Teacher support

Less confident learners: Encourage these children to estimate and count actual dominoes with up to 30 spots and partition in two ways (for example, 28: 20 + 8, 10 + 18).
More confident learners: Provide up to ten dominoes with up to 100 spots in total.

Common misconception

Children cannot partition numbers.
Provide place value equipment, and ensure that children recognise that a cube stands for 1 and a stick for 10. Show 25 using two sticks and five cubes, and ask children to split them into tens and units and write the matching number sentence.

Probing questions

- How did you make your estimate?
- Why is grouping in tens a better method than counting them all one at a time?
- How can you partition 49? What are some other ways?

Next steps

Support: Focus on grouping up to 30 objects in tens. For each number, use place value equipment to show several different ways that the number can be partitioned. See also Year 2 Block A Unit 1.
Extension: Ask the children to partition three-digit numbers in different ways (for example, 367 = 200 + 160 + 7). See also Year 2 Block A Unit 3.

Activity 4

Prior learning
Children can add or subtract a one-digit number to or from any two-digit number, including over a tens boundary. They can demonstrate their calculations on a number line and record with number sentences.

Framework objective
Add or subtract mentally a one-digit number or a multiple of 10 to or from any two-digit number; use practical and informal written methods to add or subtract two-digit numbers

Vocabulary
calculate, mental calculation, right, correct, wrong, number sentence, sign, operation, symbol, penny, pence, pound (£)

Resources
Resource sheets: Toy shop, Self-assessment
Classroom resources: plain, lined and squared paper, number lines, pound coins and/or play money

Toy shop

Give the children the toy cards cut from resource sheet 'Toy shop'. Ask them to choose two toys and find the total cost using one of these strategies: bridging 10, near doubles, adding near multiples of 10 and adjusting, counting on or partitioning. Encourage them to record in their own way using plain, lined or squared paper. Note how they tackle each calculation. Say an amount that children could spend at the toy shop and ask them to work out the change if they were to buy their two chosen toys. Decide whether to use the self-assessment sheet for children to record their achievements and what they need to do next.

Teacher support
Less confident learners: Provide only the toy cards with values up to £20 and number lines for support. The children could choose a toy under £10 and one between £10 and £20 to total.
More confident learners: Ask the children to find the total cost of three toys and give them a higher budget when asking them to calculate change.

Common misconception
Children can add and subtract but don't know which operation to use to solve a given problem.
Talk through various problems and ask questions such as: *Find the total cost. What is the change? How much more do I need to buy ___?* Ask children to use play money to find the answers, recording what they do with jottings and then as number sentences.

Probing questions
- What strategy might you use to work out 12 + 13?
- Is there another way to work this out?
- What about 25 + 26?

Next steps
Support: To reinforce and consolidate, provide the toy cards from the resource sheet 'Toy shop'. Explain that there is a sale and all the prices have been reduced by £5. Ask the children to find the new prices by counting back from the old prices. Then ask them to choose two toys and find the new total cost. Provide number lines for support. See also Year 2 Block A Unit 1.
Extension: Provide the toy cards from the resource sheet 'Toy shop'. Give the children a budget and ask them to spend as much of it as possible and to record what they do. See also Year 2 Block A Unit 3.

Activity ⑤

Prior learning
Children can solve practical problems that involve combining groups of two, five or ten, or sharing into equal groups. They can explain their methods and results, using mathematical language jottings and symbols.

Framework objective
Use the symbols +, -, ×, ÷ and = to record and interpret number sentences involving all four operations; calculate the value of an unknown in a number sentence (for example, □ ÷ 2 = 6, 30 - □ = 24)

Vocabulary
calculate, mental calculation, right, correct, wrong, number sentence, sign, operation, symbol, penny, pence, pound (£)

Resources
Display page: Symbols
Resource sheet: Self-assessment
Classroom resources: whiteboards and pens, counting objects (cubes)

⑤ Symbols

Reveal the display page 'Symbols'. Use the pen tool to write in calculations that involve a mixture of single and two-digit numbers to 50, such as 17 + □ = 22, □ - □ = 12, 10 × 3 = □, □ ÷ □ = 5. Ask the children to complete the calculations on their whiteboards and then invite those you particularly wish to observe to write the corect number into the correct space and explain how they found the answer. Decide whether to use the self-assessment sheet for children to record their achievements and what they need to do next.

Teacher support
Less confident learners: Limit the numbers up to 30 and provide counting objects.
More confident learners: Work with single-digit and two-digit numbers to 100. Encourage the children to use paper for jottings as appropriate.

Common misconceptions
Children have difficulty making links between addition and subtraction.
Provide cubes. Ask a child to count out six cubes. Then add one and ask them to count the total. Take one cube away, and ask children to predict how many they have left. They can count to check. Extend to adding and subtracting ten then other numbers of cubes.

Children have difficulty making the links between multiplication and division.
On a number line, draw different numbers of jumps of 2, 5 or 10 forward. Then count the same number of jumps back to zero to demonstrate the relationship between multiplication and division.

Probing questions
- What number goes here to make the calculation correct? How do you know?
- Can you use 3, 5 and 15 to make four different number sentences?
- How did you know that?

Next steps
Support: Focus on addition and subtraction of numbers to 20 with the missing number at the beginning of the calculation. The children could use counting objects to help them. See also Year 1 Block A Unit 3.
Extension: Ask these children to solve missing number calculations with pairs of two-digit numbers to 100, such as □ + 36 = 62, □ - 24 = 16. Encourage them to use appropriate strategies such as counting on and back. Let them use paper for jottings. See also Year 2 Block A Unit 3.

Unit 3 Counting, partitioning and calculating

Introduction

In this unit, children use their knowledge of counting on from or back to zero in steps of 2, 5 and 10 to answer multiplication and division questions. They describe patterns in sequences when counting on and back from two- or three-digit numbers. They find missing numbers in simple sequences. They estimate numbers of objects and count them in groups. They round two-digit numbers to the nearest 10. They order and compare using the symbols < and >. They use partitioning, counting strategies and number pairs to add and subtract. They use informal methods to solve problems using any of the four operations. This work is conducted through the 'using and applying' objective, with an emphasis on explaining and recording in an organised way.

Framework objectives	Assessment focuses		Success criteria for Year 2	Learning outcomes
	Level 2	Level 1		
1 It's a problem!				
Present solutions to puzzles and problems in an organised way; explain decisions, methods and results in pictorial, spoken or written form, using mathematical language and number sentences	• discuss their work using mathematical language, e.g. with support • describe the strategies and methods they use in their work • engage with others' explanations, compare... evaluate... • begin to represent their work using symbols and simple diagrams, e.g. with support • use pictures, diagrams and symbols to communicate their thinking, or demonstrate a solution or process • begin to appreciate the need to record and develop their own methods of recording • explain why an answer is correct, e.g. with support • test a statement such as, 'The number twelve ends with a 2, so 12 sweets can be shared equally between two children.'	• represent their work with objects or pictures • discuss their work, e.g. with support: • respond to questions and ideas from peers and adults • refer to the materials they have used and talk about what they have done, patterns they have noticed etc • draw simple conclusions from their work, e.g. with support • describe the different ways they have sorted objects, what is the same about objects in a set, how sets differ • identify which set has most, which object is biggest, smallest, tallest etc	• can use an efficient strategy to answer two-digit addition, subtraction, multiplication and division calculations • can show and explain how to solve a problem	*I can show and explain clearly how I solved a problem.*
2 Sequencing				
Read and write two-digit and three-digit numbers in figures and words; describe and extend number sequences and recognise odd and even numbers	• recognise sequences of numbers, including odd and even numbers, e.g. • continue a sequence that increases or decreases in regular steps • recognise numbers from counting in tens or twos	• order numbers to 10, e.g. • say what number comes next, is one more/less • count back to zero • begin to count in twos	• can recognise a pattern • can count forwards and backwards in steps of two, five or ten	*I can read and write numbers up to 1000 in figures and in words.* *I can explain the pattern for a sequence of numbers and work out the next few numbers in the list.*

Unit 3 Counting, partitioning and calculating

Framework objectives	Assessment focuses		Success criteria for Year 2	Learning outcomes
	Level 2	Level 1		
(3) Partition it!				
Count up to 100 objects by grouping them and counting in tens, fives or twos; explain what each digit in a two-digit number represents, including numbers where zero is a place holder; partition two-digit numbers in different ways, including into multiples of 10 and 1	• count sets of objects reliably, e.g. ◦ group objects in tens, twos or fives to count them • begin to understand the place value of each digit, use this to order numbers up to 100, e.g. ◦ know the relative size of numbers to 100 ◦ use zero as a place holder ◦ demonstrate knowledge using a range of models/images	• count up to 10 objects, e.g. ◦ estimate and check a number • read, write numbers to 10 ◦ perhaps with some reversal	• can partition two-digit numbers into tens and ones • can use partitioning to add or subtract	*I can use partitioning to help me to carry out calculations.*
(4) Order! Order!				
Order two-digit numbers and position them on a number line; use the greater than (>) and less than (<) signs	• begin to understand the place value of each digit, use this to order numbers up to 100, e.g. ◦ know the relative size of numbers to 100 ◦ use zero as a place holder ◦ demonstrate knowledge using a range of models/images	• order numbers to 10, e.g. ◦ say what number comes next, is one more/less ◦ count back to zero ◦ place 1-10 into ascending order ◦ point to first, second etc in a line ◦ begin to count in twos	• can order a mixed set of two-digit numbers • can position two-digit numbers on a number line • can use the symbols < and > to describe the relationship between two numbers	*I can write numbers in order and position them on a number line.* *I can use the greater than and less than symbols to show that one number is larger or smaller than another.*
(5) What a guess!				
Estimate a number of objects; round two-digit numbers to the nearest 10	• count sets of objects reliably, e.g. ◦ group objects in tens, twos or fives to count them • begin to understand the place value of each digit, use this to order numbers up to 100, e.g. ◦ know the relative size of numbers to 100	• count up to 10 objects, e.g. ◦ estimate and check a number	• can estimate quantities with increasing accuracy • can estimate where a number should go on a number line to 100	*I can say roughly how many there are in a group of objects.*

Unit 3 Counting, partitioning and calculating

Framework objectives	Assessment focuses		Success criteria for Year 2	Learning outcomes
	Level 2	Level 1		
6 Which way?				
Add or subtract mentally a one-digit number or a multiple of 10 to or from any two-digit number; use practical and informal written methods to add and subtract two-digit numbers	● use mental recall of addition and subtraction facts to 10 e.g. • use addition/subtraction facts to 10 and place value to add or subtract multiples of 10, e.g. know 3 + 7 = 10 and use place value to derive 30 + 70 = 100 ● use mental calculation strategies to solve number problems including those involving money and measures, e.g. • recall doubles to 10 + 10 and other significant doubles, e.g. double 50p is 100p or £1 • use knowledge of doubles to 10 + 10 to derive corresponding halves	● add or subtract numbers of objects to 10 • begin to add by counting on from the number of objects in the first set ● begin to know some addition facts, e.g. • doubles of numbers to double 5	● understands addition as finding the total of two or more numbers ● understands subtraction as 'taking away' and 'finding the difference'	*I can add and subtract two-digit numbers using practical equipment or written notes to help me.*
7 Inversions				
Understand that subtraction is the inverse of addition and vice versa; use this to derive and record related addition and subtraction number sentences	● use the knowledge that subtraction is the inverse of addition, e.g. • begin to understand subtraction as 'difference' • given 14, 6 and 8, make related addition and subtraction sentences ● use mental recall of addition and subtraction facts	● understand addition as finding the total of two or more sets of objects ● understand subtraction as 'taking away' objects from a set and finding how many are left	● can add or subtract single and two-digit numbers confidently using mental methods and notes to help	*I know when it is easier to use addition to work out a subtraction.*
8 What's missing?				
Use the symbols +, −, ×, ÷ and = to record and interpret number sentences involving all four operations; calculate the value of an unknown in a number sentence (e.g. □ ÷ 2 = 6, 30 - □ = 24)	● begin to represent their work using symbols and simple diagrams, e.g. with support • use pictures, diagrams and symbols to communicate their thinking ● record their work in writing, e.g. • record their mental calculations as number sentences	● record their work, e.g. • begin to use the symbols '+' and '=' to record additions	● understands how to carry out the four operations ● can use inverse operations to work out missing numbers	*I can work out the missing number in a number sentence such as 14 + □ = 35.*

Activity 1

Prior learning
Children can solve word problems using addition, subtraction, multiplication and division. They record their working as a number sentence.

Framework objective
Present solutions to puzzles and problems in an organised way; explain decisions, methods and results in pictorial, spoken or written form, using mathematical language and number sentences

Vocabulary
pattern, sequence, continue, partition, calculate, mental calculation, right, correct, wrong, number sentence, sign, operation

Resources
Resource sheets: Self-assessment, 100-square, Fruit cards, Toy shop
Classroom resources: number lines and counters, play money, paper

1 It's a problem!

Give the children plain paper to use for jottings. Ask them a variety of questions involving the four operations. For example:

- Susie spent 69p. Clara spent 23p more. How much did Clara spend?
- Shanta spent £1.50. He spent 25p more than Ian. How much did Ian spend?
- I had six pound coins. My friend had three times that many. How much money did my friend have?
- Stephen has ten £1 coins. He divided them into five equal piles. How much was in one pile?

Invite individual children to explain how they solved the problems. Decide whether to use self-assessment sheet for children to record their achievements and what they need to do next.

Teacher support
Less confident learners: Ask questions with amounts to 50p or involving whole pounds. Provide number lines or 100-squares for support.
More confident learners: Give children prices that include amounts of pounds and pence to £5. Expect them to check their work by using inverse operations.

Common misconceptions
Children do not understand the concept of multiplication.
Practise repeated addition of twos, fives or tens with groups of counters. Relate this to multiplication by setting out the appropriate number of counters and writing the calculation. For example: 2 + 2 + 2 = 2 × 4 (two, four times) = 8.

Children do not understand the concept of division as sharing.
Be very practical – for example, by using toy farm animals and sharing them into hoops representing fields. Then relate this to division by writing the matching calculation.

Probing questions
- What facts do you need to know to be able to solve the problem?
- How did you know which operation to use?
- What do your jottings show?

Next steps
Support: To reinforce and consolidate, give the children cards cut from the resource sheet 'Fruit cards'. Use these to make up similar problems to those in the activity. See also Year 2 Block A Unit 2.
Extension: Give these children the fruit cards (or toy cards cut from the resource sheet 'Toy shop'). Use these cards to create more complex two-step problems. See also Year 2 Block E Unit 3.

Activity 2

Prior learning

Children can read and write two-digit and three-digit numbers. They understand the place value in a three-digit number. They recognise patterns and make number sequences.

Framework objective

Read and write two-digit and three-digit numbers in figures and words; describe and extend number sequences and recognise odd and even numbers

Vocabulary

zero, ten, twenty..., one hundred, two hundred..., one thousand, count in ones, twos, threes, fours, fives and so on, odd, even, pattern, sequence, continue, partition

Resources

Worksheet: Sequencing
Resource sheets: 100-square, Self-assessment
Classroom resources: number lines

2 Sequencing

Begin by counting in steps of 2 from single, two-digit and three-digit numbers. Write the sequences on the board. Ask the children what they notice: the numbers in each sequence are all even numbers or all odd numbers. Repeat with steps of 10: the numbers all have the same last digit. Give each child a copy of the resource sheet '100-square'. Ask them to begin at 22 and circle every fifth number until they get to 57. They should then write that sequence, write the next three numbers and then describe what happens to the digits to a friend. Decide whether to use the self-assessment sheet for children to record their achievements and what they need to do next.

Teacher support

Less confident learners: Provide these children with copies of the worksheet 'Sequencing'. Ask them to start a sequence at 5, circling every fifth number, so reinforcing multiples of 5.
More confident learners: Provide the worksheet 'Sequencing' and ask children to explore number sequences involving counting in steps of 3 and 4.

Common misconceptions

Children count the first number as 'one' when counting on.
Place a counter on a number line and ask the child to physically move it five times and say the number they land on as they do so.

Children cannot say the number that is one more than a given number.
Ask children to count sounds silently (for example, drum beats) and move their finger along a number line as they do. Stop and ask what the next number will be. Encourage them to refer to their number line when answering.

Probing questions

- A number sequence includes 11, 13, 15, 17. What is the number before 11 and the number after 17?
- If you count in tens, which digit stays the same? Which digit changes?

Next steps

Support: Concentrate on counting different sequences in ones and tens using number lines and 100-squares. See also Year 2 Block A Unit 2.
Extension: Compare counting in tens with two-digit and three-digit numbers, identifying the digit that changes and the ones that stay the same. Discuss what happens when counting from a number such as 192 in tens, and why. See also Year 3 Block A Unit 1.

Activity 3

Prior learning

Children can make, discuss and compare estimates. They can partition two- and three-digit numbers and understand zero as a place holder.

Framework objective

Count up to 100 objects by grouping them and counting in tens, fives or twos; explain what each digit in a two-digit number represents, including numbers where zero is a place holder; partition two-digit numbers in different ways, including into multiples of 10 and 1

Vocabulary

zero, ten, twenty..., one hundred, two hundred..., one thousand, count in ones, twos, threes, fours, fives and so on, odd, even, pattern, sequence, continue, partition

Resources

Resource sheets: 0-100 numeral cards, Self-assessment, Place value arrow cards

3 Partition it!

Work with a small group of children. Begin by asking them to pick a number card and partition the number in different ways - for example, 49: 40 + 9, 30 + 19, 20 + 29. Next, say that you want to take 24 away from 49 and ask the children which of their 'partitionings' can help and why. Agree on 20 + 29, because the 20 can be taken away easily, leaving the 4 to be taken away from the remaining 29. Subtract other numbers from 49 - for example, 41, 33, 19. Repeat the activity with other number cards. Decide whether to use the self-assessment sheet for children to record their achievements and what they need to do next.

Teacher support

Less confident learners: Use number cards to 30, asking the children to partition in two ways (for example, 28: 20 + 8, 10 + 18). Ask them to subtract 23 from 28, then 17, by choosing the appropriate children to partition three-digit numbers into hundreds, tens and units.

More confident learners: Encourage these children to answer calculations by partitioning the numbers in different ways. For example, for 49 - 24 they partition 49 into 24 and 25 so that they can take the 24 away directly.

Common misconceptions

Children cannot partition numbers into tens and units.

Use place value arrow cards to make a number (such as 48). Demonstrate how to separate the cards to show the tens and units. Write the number sentence: 48 = 40 + 8. Ask children to repeat this exercise for different two-digit numbers.

Children cannot use partitioning when subtracting.

Provide two tens and two units place value arrow cards. Ask children to make the largest and smallest numbers possible. Show them how to subtract the smaller number by subtracting first the units and then the tens.

Probing questions

- How could you partition 26 and 44 to add them?
- Which partitioning would be best to answer 34 - 26?
- How would you solve this?

Next steps

Support: Focus on partitioning numbers to 40 and addition. See also Year 2 Block A Unit 2.

Extension: Work on addition and subtraction of three-digit numbers, using the partitioning method in the activity. See also Year 3 Block A Unit 1.

Activity 4

Prior learning

Children can use place value to order numbers. They can use the symbols < and > to compare numbers. They can position numbers on a number line marked in 10s.

Framework objective

Order two-digit numbers and position them on a number line; use the greater than (>) and less than (<) signs

Vocabulary

compare, order, larger, greater than, smaller, less than, between, half-way between, difference between, round, nearest ten, tens boundary, roughly, about the same as

Resources

Resource sheets: 0-50 number lines, Self-assessment, 0-9 digit cards
Classroom resources: Blu-Tack®, whiteboards and pens

4 Order! Order!

Ask the children to use digit cards to make five two-digit numbers and to place them where they think they would go on an imaginary number line on their table. Draw a line on the board and mark 0 and 100 at either end. Invite the children to place one of their numbers onto the number line. Write a two-digit number on the board (for example, 54) and ask the children to compare their numbers with it, using the symbols < and >, writing these on their whiteboards. Decide whether to use the self-assessment sheet for children to record their achievements and what they need to do next.

Teacher support

Less confident learners: Ask these children to make numbers to 50 with their digit cards and order these. Provide numbered number lines as support. Ask them which numbers are greater/less than 30. Record their numbers using the appropriate symbol (< or >).
More confident learners: Challenge these children to make five different three-digit numbers, to write them down, order them and compare them using the less than and greater than signs.

Common misconceptions

Children are not confident ordering numbers.
Provide five number cards to 30 and ask children to order them. Provide a number line for support. Ask children to pick two numbers and say which is the greater.

Children are not confident using the symbols < and >.
Draw the 'greater than' symbol (>) on the board. Provide two number cards to 30 and ask children to use Blu-Tack® to stick them correctly either side of the sign. Ask children to read the number sentence aloud, drawing over the symbol as they do so. Repeat with examples using the 'less than' sign (<).

Probing questions

- What number is greater than 59 but less than 61?
- Which numbers could you use to make this correct? □ + □ < 32
- Which numbers could you use to make this correct? □ + □ > 51

Next steps

Support: Focus on ordering numbers to 20 on a blank number line. Compare pairs of numbers using either the 'less than' or the 'greater than' symbol. See also Year 2 Block A Unit 1.
Extension: Place mixed two-digit and three-digit numbers on an empty number line to 1000. Next, ask children to choose pairs of numbers and compare them using the 'less than' and 'greater than' symbols. See also Year 3 Block A Unit 1.

Activity 5

Prior learning

Children can estimate a number of objects and check their estimates by counting in groups of two, five or ten. They can use the correct vocabulary to round their estimate to a multiple of ten.

Framework objective

Estimate a number of objects; round two-digit numbers to the nearest ten

Vocabulary

estimate, roughly, about the same as, round, nearest ten

Resources

Worksheets: What a guess! (1) and (2)
Resource sheet: Self-assessment
Classroom resources: whiteboards and pens, pots of up to 100 counters

5 What a guess!

Give each child a pot of up to 100 counters. Ask them to tip them onto the table and estimate how many there are, writing their estimates on their whiteboards. Next, ask them to count them by grouping in tens. Once they have counted about half, ask the children to look at their estimates and decide whether they want to change them. They can then carry on counting. Give opportunities for them to adjust their estimates as they go. Once they have finished, ask them to compare the actual amount to their estimate. Decide whether to use the self-assessment resource sheet for children to record their achievements and what they need to do next.

Teacher support

Less confident learners: Work with numbers to 20. Provide the children with a pile of ten counters and ask them to make their estimates using the pile of ten.
More confident learners: Give the children several opportunities to estimate, and assess whether they become more accurate the more often they try.

Common misconceptions

Children have difficulty understanding the concept of estimating.
Give real-life examples of why estimating is helpful (for example, estimating rough answers when calculating, estimating total cost when shopping). When children sees a purpose for this, they are more likely to begin to understand.

Children have difficulty estimating.
Provide the worksheet 'What a guess! (1)'. Show a card and ask children to count how many spots there are. Show another card and ask children to estimate whether there are more or fewer dots on that card than the first before asking children to estimate the number of dots on the second card.

Probing questions

- How did you make your estimate?
- What information did you use?
- What helped you to decide?

Next steps

Support: Provide five cards from the worksheet 'What a guess! (1)', and ask the children to place them in order, estimating how many spots there are on each. See also Year 2 Block A Unit 1.
Extension: Focus on estimating over 100 items. Give the children one of the cards from the worksheet 'What a guess! (2)' and ask them to estimate how many dots there are altogether. They note their estimate and then count in tens by grouping dots. Encourage them to adjust their estimates if necessary as they go along. See also Year 2 Block D Unit 2.

Activity 6

Prior learning
Children can count on from and back to any number in ones, including across tens and hundreds boundaries. They can add/subtract nine to/from a two-digit number by adding/subtracting ten then adjusting.

Framework objective
Add or subtract mentally a one-digit number or a multiple of 10 to or from any two-digit number; use practical and informal written methods to add and subtract two-digit numbers

Vocabulary
calculate, mental calculation, right, correct, wrong, number sentence, sign, operation, symbol, penny, pence, pound (£)

Resources
Resource sheets: 0-100 numeral cards, Self-assessment, 100-square

6 Which way?

Show a number card, and ask the children to add and then subtract 9 by adding or subtracting 10 and adjusting, recording their method on paper. Repeat using other numbers. Show a number and this time ask the children to add 9 by using their knowledge of number bonds to 10 to get to the next multiple of 10, and to record their calculation. For example: 43 + 9 = (43 + 7) + 2 = 52. Repeat this several times. *Which strategy did you prefer? Why?* Decide whether to use the self-assessment sheet for children to record their achievements and what they need to do next.

Teacher support
Less confident learners: Provide the resource sheet '100-square' to help the children to add and subtract 9. Encourage them to move forward or back 10 and then subtract or add 1.
More confident learners: Ask these children to add and subtract two-digit numbers ending with 9 to the number you show.

Common misconceptions
Children cannot 'read' a 100-square.
Cut a 100-square into strips and lay the strips out as a number line. Re-make the square, saying that it is a number line that is read like a book.

Children have difficulty remembering number bonds to 10.
When practising number bonds to 10, put them into context. For example: *I have £1. I need £10 to buy the toy. How much more do I need?*

Probing questions
- How would you work out 36 + 8? Is there another way?
- What can help you work out 43 - 9? Is there anything else?
- Which number facts will help you to work out 28 + 7?

Next steps
Support: To reinforce and consolidate, concentrate on the strategy of using number bonds to make the next multiple of 10. See also Year 2 Block A Unit 2.
Extension: Encourage the children to add single-digit and then two-digit numbers that end with 8 by adding the next multiple of 10 and adding or subtracting 2. See also Year 2 Block D Unit 3.

Activity 7

Prior learning

Children understand that addition can be done in any order. They understand subtraction as 'take away' and counting back, and they can find a difference by counting up. They understand that addition and subtraction are inverse operations.

Framework objective

Understand that subtraction is the inverse of addition and vice versa; use this to derive and record related addition and subtraction number sentences

Vocabulary

addition, subtraction, inverse, calculate, mental calculation, right, correct, wrong, number sentence, sign, operation, symbol, penny, pence, pound (£)

Resources

Worksheet: Inversions
Classroom resources: whiteboards and pens, 0-20 number lines, counters or counting objects

7 Inversions

Write this number sentence on the board: 24 - 7 = 17. Ask the children to write the three associated number sentences on their whiteboards. Repeat with another addition or subtraction. Once they are familiar with this, pose some problems that involve using this knowledge. For example: *I have some pound coins. My friend gave me two more and now I have 12. How many did I start with?* Give a set of cards cut from the worksheet 'Inversions' to each pair of children. Ask them to sort the cards into those that can more easily be answered by addition and those that are best subtracted and then to answer them.

Teacher support

Less confident learners: Use the cards from the worksheet 'Inversions' that involve addition or subtraction using a units number. Together, find the answers. Discuss whether it is best to add or subtract, and why.
More confident learners: Ask these children to make up their own cards for a partner to solve.

Common misconceptions

Children have difficulty understanding that addition and subtraction are inverse operations.
Provide a 0-20 number line. Ask children to put a counter on a number. Then ask them to add 5 to the number, and write the number sentence. Now ask them to subtract 5. Repeat and point out the pattern of inverse operations.

Children do not recognise that addition can be done in any order.
Using counting objects, demonstrate that 7 + 9 gives the same answer as 9 + 7.

Probing questions

- I start with 5 and end with 18. What have I done?
- How did you work that out?
- How can you check?

Next steps

Support: To reinforce, use a number line to demonstrate inversions. Once the children are confident with this, replace the number line with a loop diagram, which is an easily remembered visual image. See also Year 2 Block A Unit 1.
Extension: Ask these children to make up some 'I am thinking of...' questions to ask each other. For example: *I am thinking of a number. I take away 13. I have 14 left. What was my original number?* See also Year 3 Block A Unit 1.

Activity 8

Prior learning
Children understand that addition and subtraction are inverse operations, as are multiplication and division. They use jottings to help them calculate.

Framework objective
Use the symbols +, -, ×, ÷ and = to record and interpret number sentences involving all four operations; calculate the value of an unknown in a number sentence (for example, □ ÷ 2 = 6, 30 - □ = 24)

Vocabulary
calculate, mental calculation, right, correct, wrong, number sentence, sign, operation, symbol, penny, pence, pound (£)

Resources
Worksheets: What's missing? (1), (2) and (3)
Resource sheet: Self-assessment
Classroom resources: counters or counting objects, number lines

8 What's missing?

Provide the cards cut from the worksheet 'What's missing? (1)'. Work with the group of children you wish to assess and observe how they work out the missing numbers. Ask them to explain their methods. Keep a record of their jottings. Decide whether to use the self-assessment sheet for children to record their achievements and what they need to do next.

Teacher support
Less confident learners: Use the cards from the worksheet 'What's missing? (2)', which involve numbers less than 30. Provide counting objects for children to use as support.
More confident learners: Use the cards from the worksheet 'What's missing? (3)', which include numbers greater than 100.

Common misconceptions
Children cannot identify how to find a missing number.
Work with numbers to 10, focusing on addition initially. Provide counters for children to 'set out' the calculation, leaving a space for the missing number. Encourage them to realise that the missing number will be less than the answer.

Children have difficulty making links between multiplication and division.
Use a number line to make different jumps of 2, 5 or 10. Then make the jumps backwards to zero, so reinforcing the inverse relationship between multiplication and division.

Probing questions
- What is the missing number? How did you work that out?
- Is there another way you could have done this?
- How many ways can you think of to add and subtract three numbers to make 20?

Next steps
Support: To reinforce and consolidate, concentrate on missing numbers in sentences involving addition and subtraction of numbers to 30. Encourage appropriate strategies such as counting on for the first example and addition of known numbers for the second. See also Year 2 Block A Unit 2.
Extension: As an investigation, challenge the children to find ways to add, subtract, multiply and divide two numbers to give an answer of 50 and then 100. See also Year 2 Block E Unit 3.

Units 1, 2 & 3 Periodic assessment

These activities can be used at the end of this block to assess those children that you think have achieved the objectives.

Counting numbers and partitioning

Framework objective

Count up to 100 objects by grouping them and counting in tens, fives or twos; explain what each digit in a two-digit number represents, including numbers where zero is a place holder; partition two-digit numbers in different ways, including into multiples of ten and one

Learning outcomes

- I can count objects by putting them into groups.
- I can partition numbers.
- I can explain what each digit in a two-digit number stands for.
- I can partition numbers in different ways.
- I can use partitioning to help me to carry out calculations.

There are three activities for this objective.

1. Give the children copies of the worksheet 'Counting numbers and partitioning'. Ask them to count the stars. Sit with the group of children you particularly wish to assess and observe how they do this. Do they draw loops around five or ten stars at a time? Do they count them one at a time, marking them as they go along?

2. Give the children place value arrow cards and ask them to make different two-digit numbers. Once they have done this, ask them to explain the value of each digit. Next, say some numbers for them to write, then ask them to partition them in different ways. For example, for 65: 60 + 5, 50 + 15, 40 + 25, 30 + 35, 20 + 45, 10 + 55. Sit with the group of children you particularly wish to assess and observe how they do this. How confident are they?

3. Sit with the group of children you particularly wish to assess. Say some two-digit numbers and observe how confidently they partition them in different ways. Provide 1–20 numeral cards. Ask the children to pick two cards and find their total using a partitioning method. Then ask them to subtract the smaller number from the larger one. Do they use partitioning or prefer to count on? If they partition, do they do this in different ways? For example, for 46 – 24, do they partition 46 into 20 and 26, take away the 20 and then the 4? Make notes and use these to inform your next steps.

Units 1, 2 & 3 Periodic assessment

In my head

Framework objective

Add or subtract mentally a single-digit number or a multiple of ten to or from any two-digit number; use practical and informal written methods to add or subtract two-digit numbers

Learning outcomes

- I can add and subtract some numbers in my head.
- I can add and subtract bigger numbers using practical equipment or by writing notes to help me.

There are three activities for this objective.

1. Give each child two sets of number cards cut from the resource sheet 'In my head'. One set of cards consists of single-digit numbers and the other contains two-digit numbers. The children pick one card from each pile then use a mental method to find the total of the numbers and then their difference. You may wish to remind them of the possible methods for addition. Encourage bridging 10, near doubles, adding near multiples of 10 and adjusting, counting on and partitioning. Provide the worksheet 'In my head (1)' for the children to record their methods and answers.

2. Ask the children to say the different strategies for calculating totals and differences. To find totals they should consider using knowledge of number bonds to make the next multiple of 10, adding 9 by adding 10 and adjusting, and also partitioning. To find a difference they should consider counting back from the larger number or counting on from the smallest number. Give each child a copy of worksheet 'In my head (2)'. Ask them to choose pairs of toys and find the total cost, showing their thinking in the way that suits them. Provide counters or pound coins in case the children wish to use them. Observe how targeted children work, particularly how they answer the second question.

3. Ask the children to say the different strategies for calculating totals and differences: using knowledge of number bonds to make the next multiple of 10, adding 9 by adding 10 and adjusting, partitioning, counting on or back. Give each child a copy of worksheet 'In my head (3)', which requires them to pick pairs of numbers to total and find the difference. Sit with a group of children on whom you wish to focus and observe. Do they need bead strings or number lines? If so, how do they use them? Are they able to make notes and/or diagrams? Can they use these to show clearly their thinking?

Name Date

In my head (1)

Cut out the cards from the resource sheet 'In my head'.

- Place the numbers into one-digit and two-digit piles.
- Pick a card from each pile.
- Find the total of your numbers.
- Find the difference between your numbers.

Numbers: ______

Total: ______

Difference: ______

Numbers: ______

Total: ______

Difference: ______

Numbers: ______

Total: ______

Difference: ______

How easy?

Red
Amber
Green

How do you think you have done?

______

______

Name Date

In my head (2)

1. Choose pairs of toys and work out how much they cost.

1st toy costs ____________
2nd toy costs ____________
Total cost ____________
How did you work this out?

1st toy costs ____________
2nd toy costs ____________
Total cost ____________
How did you work this out?

1st toy costs ____________
2nd toy costs ____________
Total cost ____________
How did you work this out?

1st toy costs ____________
2nd toy costs ____________
Total cost ____________
How did you work this out?

2. How much more is the dolls' house than each of these?

a) the teddy ____________ **b)** the dinosaur ____________

c) the digger ____________

How easy?

Red
Amber
Green

How do you think you have done?

____

____

BLOCK A

Name Date

In my head (3)

- Choose pairs of numbers.
- Find the total of the numbers in each pair.
- Find the difference of the numbers in each pair.

26	48	59	18	72	34	14

My numbers are

_________ and _________.

Total _________

Difference _________

My numbers are

_________ and _________.

Total _________

Difference _________

My numbers are

_________ and _________.

Total _________

Difference _________

My numbers are

_________ and _________.

Total _________

Difference _________

How easy?

Red
Amber
Green

How do you think you have done?

____

____

BLOCK B

Securing number facts, understanding shape

Expected prior learning

Check that children can already:

- describe simple patterns and relationships involving numbers or shapes
- solve problems involving counting, adding, subtracting, doubling or halving in the context of numbers, measures or money; recognise the value of coins
- recall addition and subtraction facts to 10 and doubles of all numbers to at least 10
- use informal written methods to add or subtract a one-digit number or multiple of 10 to or from a two-digit number, recording an addition or subtraction number sentence
- name common 2D shapes and 3D solids and describe their features
- use diagrams to sort objects into groups according to a given criterion.

Objectives overview

The text in this diagram identifies the focus of mathematics learning within the block.

Key aspects of learning

- Problem solving
- Creative thinking
- Information processing
- Motivation

Patterns, relationships and properties of numbers and shapes

Solving problems involving numbers, money or measures, using addition, subtraction, multiplication and division

Estimating and checking answers

BLOCK B: Securing number facts, understanding shape

Addition and subtraction facts to 10; pairs that sum to 20; multiples of 10 that sum to 100

Tables for 2, 5 and 10

Doubles of numbers to 10; corresponding halves

Describing and visualising properties of common 2D and 3D shapes

Line symmetry

Sorting and making shapes

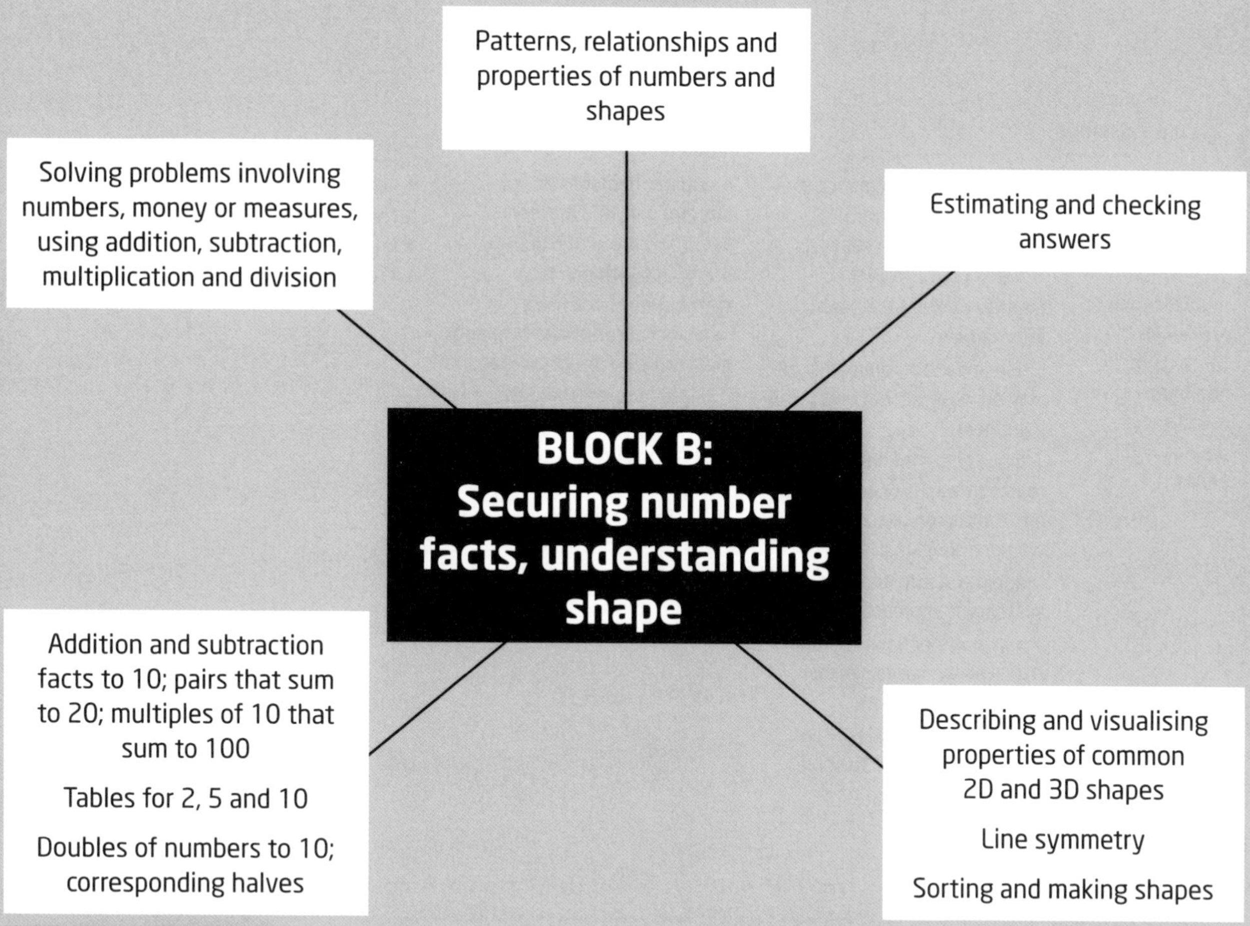

Unit 1 Securing number facts, understanding shape

BLOCK B

Introduction

In this unit, children are encouraged to use and apply taught skills, listen to others, ask relevant questions and follow instructions. They make use of addition and subtraction facts, multiples of 2, 5 and 10 and doubles and halves, to estimate and check calculations and problems involving the four operations in different contexts. They read and write two- and three-digit numbers, explore number sequences and recognise odd and even numbers. They visualise common 2D shapes and 3D solids and can identify them from pictures in different orientations. They sort, make and describe shapes, referring to their properties.

Framework objectives	Assessment focuses: Level 2	Assessment focuses: Level 1	Success criteria for Year 2	Learning outcomes
1 Patterns and relationships				
Describe patterns and relationships involving numbers or shapes, make predictions and test these with examples	• predict what comes next in a simple number, shape or spatial pattern or sequence and give reasons for their opinions	• recognise and use a simple pattern or relationship, e.g. with support • copy and continue a simple pattern of objects, shapes or numbers	• can identify shape sequences, saying what the shape will be several places ahead of those seen • can recognise and continue simple number sequences • can describe their sequences	*I can sort a set of 3D shapes.* *I can continue a number pattern.* *I can explain how I know.*
2 Coin exchange				
Solve problems involving addition, subtraction, multiplication or division in contexts of numbers, measures or pounds and pence	• select the mathematics they use in some classroom activities, e.g. with support • find a starting point, identifying key facts/relevant information • use apparatus, diagrams, role play etc to represent and clarify a problem • move between different representations of a problem e.g. a situation described in words, a diagram etc • adopt a suggested model or systematic approach • make connections and apply their knowledge to similar situations • use mathematical content from levels 1 and 2 to solve problems and investigate	• use mathematics as an integral part of classroom activities, e.g. with support • engage with practical mathematical activities involving sorting, counting and measuring by direct comparison • begin to understand the relevance of mathematical ideas to everyday situations by using them in role-play	• can identify the coins in our monetary system • knows the value of each coin to £1	*I can solve a problem involving money.*

Unit 1 Securing number facts, understanding shape

Framework objectives	Assessment focuses		Success criteria for Year 2	Learning outcomes
	Level 2	Level 1		
3 Number facts				
Derive and recall all addition and subtraction facts for each number to at least 10, all pairs with totals to 20 and all pairs of multiples of 10 with totals up to 100	• use mental recall of addition and subtraction facts to 10, e.g. • use addition/subtraction facts to 10 and place value to add or subtract multiples of 10, e.g. know 3 + 7 = 10 and use place value to derive 30 + 70 = 100	• add or subtract numbers of objects to 10 • begin to add by counting on from the number of objects in the first set	• can add or subtract single-digit numbers • can recall addition and subtraction facts to 10 • can recognise multiples of 10	*I can recall number facts for each number up to 10.*
4 Multiple identity				
Derive and recall multiplication facts for the 2-, 5- and 10-times tables and the related division facts; recognise multiples of 2, 5 and 10	• recognise sequences of numbers, including odd and even numbers, e.g. • continue a sequence that increases or decreases in regular steps • recognise numbers from counting in tens or twos	• order numbers to 10 • say what number comes next, is one more/less	• can say what the next multiple of 2, 5 or 10 will be in a sequence • can continue a count of multiples of 2, 5 or 10 • can say the multiples of 2, 5 or 10 in order to the tenth multiple	*I can count in steps of 2, 5 or 10.*
5 Doubling and halving				
Understand that halving is the inverse of doubling, and derive and recall doubles of all numbers to 20, and the corresponding halves	• use mental calculation strategies to solve number problems including those involving money and measures, e.g. • recall doubles to 10 + 10 and other significant doubles, e.g. double 50p is 100p or £1 • use knowledge of doubles to 10 + 10 to derive corresponding halves	• begin to know some addition facts e.g. • doubles of numbers to double 5	• understands the concept of doubling • understands the concept of halving • can recall doubles to 20	*I know that if I double a number then halve the answer I get back to the number I started with.*
6 Number facts and operations				
Use knowledge of number facts and operations to estimate and check answers to calculations	• use mental recall of addition and subtraction facts to 10, e.g. • use addition/subtraction facts to 10 and place value to add or subtract multiples of 10, e.g. know 3 + 7 = 10, and use place value to derive 30 + 70 = 100	• add or subtract numbers of objects to 10 • begin to add by counting on from the number of objects in the first set	• understands the concept of addition and subtraction • can add or subtract a single-digit number to or from a two-digit number	*I can check the answer to an addition by a doing a related subtraction.*

Unit 1 Securing number facts, understanding shape

Framework objectives	Assessment focuses		Success criteria for Year 2	Learning outcomes
	Level 2	Level 1		
(7) 2D shapes (8) 3D shapes				
Visualise common 2D shapes and 3D solids; identify shapes from pictures of them in different positions and orientations; sort, make and describe shapes, referring to their properties	• use mathematical names for common 3D and 2D shapes, e.g. • identify 2D and 3D shapes from pictures of them in different orientations, e.g. square, triangle, hexagon, pentagon, octagon, cube, cylinder, sphere, cuboid, pyramid • describe their properties, including numbers of sides and corners, e.g. • make and talk about shapes referring to features and properties using language such as edge, face, corner • sort 2D and 3D shapes according to a single criterion, e.g. shapes that are pentagons or shapes with a right angle • visualise frequently used 2D and 3D shapes • begin to understand the difference between shapes with two dimensions and those with three • recognise the properties that are the same even when a shape is enlarged, e.g. when comparing squares, circles, similar triangles, cubes or spheres of different sizes	• use everyday language to describe properties of 2D and 3D shapes, e.g. • sort shapes and say how they have selected them • use properties such as large/ small, triangles, roll/stack • begin to refer to some features of shapes, such as side and corner • begin to name the shapes they use in the context of an activity	• can name common 2D and 3D shapes • can describe the features of 2D and 3D shapes • can sort objects into groups according to a given criterion	*I can look at pictures of 2D and 3D shapes and name them.*

Activity 1

Prior learning
Children can describe simple patterns and relationships involving numbers or shapes.

Framework objective
Describe patterns and relationships involving numbers or shapes, make predictions and test these with examples

Vocabulary
explain, predict, reason, pattern, relationship

Resources
Resource sheet: Self-assessment
Classroom resources: different-coloured counters, whiteboards and pens, different shapes

1 Patterns and relationships

Give the children counters of two different colours. Ask them to make different repeating patterns. Encourage them to think of interesting ways to do this. Once they have each made a pattern, ask them to describe it. Then ask them to predict what the 15th pattern in the sequence will be and to test out their prediction. Record their responses. Repeat the activity using numbers. Ask the children to write a sequence on their whiteboards. You could give an example such as: 1 4 3 6 (odd and even) or 1 2 3 1 2 3 1 2 3. Decide whether to use the self-assessment sheet for children to record their achievements and what they need to do next.

Teacher support
Less confident learners: Show a simple pattern such as 'one red, two blue, one red, two blue' and ask children to continue it. They can then make their own patterns.
More confident learners: Provide counters in three colours for children to use to make a sequence and record on paper.

Common misconception
Children cannot make a sequence.
Use counters in two colours to make a simple sequence (for example, red, blue, red, blue) and ask children to continue it. Once they have done this correctly, start a more complicated sequence for children to continue (for example, 1, 2, 3, 1, 2, 3) and ask children to continue it.

Probing questions
- If my sequence is 'circle, square, circle, square...', what is the eleventh shape? How did you work that out?
- A number sequence is 2, 4, 6, 8... What would the tenth number be? How do you know?

Next steps
Support: Work with the children to make simple shape or number sequences. Provide some shapes of two different types and ask them to set out a sequence. See also Year 1 Block B Unit 3.
Extension: Show the beginning of a sequence and ask children to predict what the tenth shape or number will be. Encourage them to look for a pattern rather than writing the sequence. For example, for 1, 2, 2, 3, 3, 3, the tenth number will be 4 because there will be four 4s. See also Year 2 Block B Unit 2.

Activity 2

Prior learning
Children can solve problems involving counting, adding, subtracting, doubling or halving in the context of numbers, measures or money.

Framework objective
Solve problems involving addition, subtraction, multiplication or division in contexts of numbers, measures or pounds and pence

Vocabulary
problem, solution, calculate, calculation, operation, inverse, answer, method, explain, predict, reason, add, subtract, multiply, divide, sum, total, difference, plus, minus

Resources
Resource sheets: Self-assessment, 0–30 numeral cards
Classroom resources: 1p, 2p, 5p and 10p coins, paper for recording

2 Coin exchange

Give the children a pile of 38 pennies and ask them to count them. Observe and make a note of how they do this: do they count in ones or twos or group in tens or fives. Once they have counted, ask them to exchange the pennies for 10p, 5p and 2p coins. Observe how they do this, making a note of those who cannot so that you can work with them at a future date. Next pose problems such as: *Sam has 15p; what coins might he have?* Ask them to record their answers in their own way. Decide whether to use the self-assessment sheet for children to record their achievements and what they need to do next.

Teacher support
Less confident learners: Give these children 20 pennies and ask them to count out 10. *What coin could we use instead?* Exchange the ten pennies for a 10p coin. Repeat with other coin equivalents.
More confident learners: Give these children 39 pennies and 20p, 10p, 5p and 2p coins. *Exchange the pennies for the fewest possible coins.*

Common misconception
Children cannot count objects up to 20.
Provide real-life objects and number cards to 20 with dots as a visual. Ask the child to count out a particular number of objects. Say you want six and ask them to count six into your hand. Repeat for other amounts.

Probing questions
- How many 2p coins are needed to make 12p?
- How did you solve the problem?
- If I have 23p, what is the smallest number of coins I could have?

Next steps
Support: Once the children understand exchanging ten pennies for a 10p coin, work on five pennies for a 5p coin, then combine different numbers of 5p coins to make 10p, 15p, 20p etc. Link with counting in fives and 5-times table facts. See also Year 1 Block B Unit 3.
Extension: Invite these children to make amounts of money using the smallest number of coins (for example, 56p = 50p + 5p + 1p). Include amounts that involve £1 and £2. See also Year 2 Block B Unit 2.

Activity 3

Prior learning
Children can recall addition and subtraction facts to 10 and doubles of all numbers to at least 10.

Framework objective
Derive and recall all addition and subtraction facts for each number to at least 10, all pairs with totals to 20 and all pairs of multiples of 10 with totals up to 100

Vocabulary
add, subtract, sum, total, difference, plus, minus

Resources
Resource sheet: Self-assessment
Classroom resources: pendulum made from three interlocking cubes on a piece of string, counting items

3 Number facts

Swing the pendulum from side to side. As it swings one way, call out a number to 10; as it swings the other way, the children call out the number that, with your number, makes 10. Focus on the children you wish to assess and make a note of the way they respond. Write on the board: □ + ○ = 9. Give the children one minute to write as many possible pairs of numbers that could go in the shapes as they can. Repeat for other additions, then some subtractions. Again, observe children's responses and note names of those who are unsure in order to work with them as a focus group in future. Decide whether to use the self-assessment sheet for children to record their achievements and what they need to do next.

Teacher support
Less confident learners: Give the children ten counters. Take five away. *How many are left?* Do the children count the counters or can they say the answer straight off? Repeat, removing different numbers of counters.
More confident learners: Say a multiple of 10 and ask the children to say the number that is needed to make 100.

Common misconception
Children are not confident recalling number pairs that total 10.
Provide concrete models to illustrate number pairs that make 10 (for example, bead strings, a coat hanger with ten clothes pegs attached). Ask the children to pull two beads or pegs to one side and count how many are left and write the corresponding number sentence: 2 + 8 = 10. Repeat for other pairs.

Probing questions
- Look at this number sentence. What could the two missing numbers be?
- What else could they be?
- Can you show me all the pairs that make 9?
- How do you know you have told me them all?

Next steps
Support: Use fingers, beads and toy animals to help children to visualise number pairs that make 10. Pose real-life problems, such as: *I had 10p and spent 6p on a lolly. How much did I have left?* See also Year 1 Block B Unit 3.
Extension: Focus on pairs of multiples of 10 with totals up to 100. Ask: *How can knowing number pairs to 10 help with this?* Repeat for number facts to 20. See also Year 2 Block B Unit 2.

Activity 4

Prior learning
Children can count on or back in ones, twos, fives and tens and derive the multiples of two, five and ten to the tenth multiple.

Framework objective
Derive and recall multiplication facts for the 2-, 5- and 10-times tables and the related division facts; recognise multiples of 2, 5 and 10

Vocabulary
multiply, divide, double, doubled, multiple, odd, even

Resources
Resource sheets: 0-100 numeral cards, Self-assessment, 0-50 number lines, 100-square
Classroom resources: Blu-Tack®, whiteboards and pens

4 Multiple identity

Stick the number card for 30 on the board. Ask the children to write the next multiple of 10 on their whiteboards and, when you say *Show me*, to hold their boards up for you to see. Repeat for the multiple of 10 before 30, the multiples of 5 after and before 30, and the even numbers after and before 30. Stick up the cards for 20, 25 and 30. Say to the children: *Continue the sequence as far as you can.* Repeat for 28, 26, 24, and for 60, 70, 80. Decide whether to use the self-assessment sheet for children to record their achievements and what they need to do next.

Teacher support
Less confident learners: Provide the 0-50 number lines as support and focus on multiples of 2, 5 and 10 up to 50.
More confident learners: Ask these children to give the three multiples of 10 that come after and before 80. Repeat for multiples of 5 and of 2.

Common misconception
Children cannot say a particular multiple of 10 but have to count up from 10.
Show a 0-100 number line that is marked in tens. Practise counting forwards and backwards in tens from zero to 100. Hide the line and practise counting again. Provide a set of cards showing the multiples of 10. Shuffle them and ask children to put them in order. Write 60 on the board. *Hold up the multiple of 10 that is 10 more than 60..., 10 less than 60.* Repeat for other multiples of 10.

Probing questions
- What is the multiple of 10 before 70?
- What three numbers come next in this sequence? 35, 40, 45...
- What is the next even number after 24?

Next steps
Support: Provide opportunities for the children to count in tens, fives and twos (for example, when using coins to pay for items in the class shop). As the shop assistant, say that one item costs 10p, 5p or 2p more than something else. Ask: *How much does it cost?* See also Year 1 Block E Unit 3.
Extension: Ask these children to explore the multiples of 2, 5 and 10 on a 100-square by colouring them in. What do they notice about the multiples of 10? (They are also multiples of 2 and 5.) See also Year 2 Block B Unit 2.

Activity 5

Prior learning
Children can solve problems involving counting, adding, subtracting, doubling or halving in the context of numbers, measures or money.

Framework objective
Understand that halving is the inverse of doubling and derive and recall doubles of all numbers to 20, and the corresponding halves

Vocabulary
add, multiply, inverse, halve, halved, double, doubled

Resources
Resource sheets: 0-10 digit cards, Self-assessment
Classroom resources: counters, whiteboards and pens

5 Doubling and halving

Call out numbers to 20 and ask the children to write their doubles on their whiteboards. Repeat for even numbers to 40, this time asking for their halves. Make a note of children who cannot do this in order to work with them as a focus group in future. Give the children a set of digit cards each. Ask them to pick a card, double it and then write an appropriate number sentence (for example, 4 + 4 = 8, double 4 = 8). Once they have done this, ask them to write the inverse statement: 8 - 4 = 4, half 8 = 4. Decide whether to use the self-assessment sheet for children to record their achievements and what they need to do next.

Teacher support
Less confident learners: Give these children ten counters, and ask them to find half. Put the groups of five together again, linking to doubling. Invite the children to say: *Half of 10 is 5; double 5 is 10.* Repeat for other numbers to 10.
More confident learners: Extend to multiples of 10 to 100.

Common misconception
Children do not recognise what 'half' is.
Provide concrete models to illustrate (for example, a biscuit, plastic farm animals and a loop to represent a field). Ask the children to break the biscuit in half. Tell them that a farmer has six horses and wants to put half that number in the field. Focus on two equal amounts. Repeat for other situations.

Probing questions
- I think of a number and double it; my answer is 24. What was my starting number? How did you work that out?
- I think of a number and halve it; my answer is 8. What was my number? How do you know?

Next steps
Support: Focus on doubles and halves of numbers to 10. Use money, beads and/or toy animals, and double and halve sets of them, linking the two as inverse operations. Pose some real-life problems. For example: *I had £3. My friend had double that amount. Show me how much she had.* See also Year 1 Block B Unit 3.
Extension: Focus on numbers to 50. Pose questions such as: *I'm thinking of a number. I've doubled it and the answer is 28. What number was I thinking of?* Ask the children to explain how they know. See also Year 2 Block E Unit 1.

Activity 6

Prior learning

Children can use written methods to add or subtract a one-digit number or multiple of ten to or from a two-digit number, and write a number sentence.

Framework objective

Use knowledge of number facts and operations to estimate and check answers to calculations

Vocabulary

solution, calculate, calculation, operation, inverse, answer, method, explain, predict, reason, add, subtract, multiply, divide, sum, total, difference, plus, minus, halve, halved, double, doubled

Resources

Resource sheet: Self-assessment
Classroom resources: whiteboards and pens, counters

6 Number facts and operations

Write this number sentence on the board: 6 + 9 = 15. Say to the children: *Write down three other number sentences using these numbers.* Observe how they respond, making a note of any children who can't write the associated sentences: 9 + 6 = 15, 15 - 9 = 6, 15 - 6 = 9. Next ask for the answer to 26 + 9 and ask how they can use the original number sentence to help, then how they can check their answer. Repeat for other calculations, such as 8 + 5 and 28 + 5, 13 + 4 and 33 + 4. Decide whether to use the self-assessment sheet for children to record their achievements and what they need to do next.

Teacher support

Less confident learners: Work with numbers to 20. Provide apparatus and model writing pairs of inverse number sentences for the children (for example, 6 + 4 = 10, 10 - 4 = 6).
More confident learners: Extend to numbers to 100.

Common misconceptions

Children are not confident that addition can be done in any order.
Model 3 + 2 and 2 + 3 using counters and write the associated number sentences.

Children cannot make the link between addition and subtraction.
Use a numbered 0–10 number line. Ask children to point to 3 and jump on 2. What number have they landed on? Use counters to confirm: *Take three. Add two.*

Probing questions

- We have worked out that 3 + 5 = 8 and 13 + 5 = 18. Without calculating, tell me what 23 + 5 will be.
- What about 63 + 5?
- What else can you work out?

Next steps

Support: Focus on using the number line to add, then checking the answer by subtracting. Check that the children return to the starting number. Each time write the number sentences and draw an inversion loop. See also Year 1 Block B Unit 3.
Extension: Using four digit cards, ask the children to write a two-digit addition calculation, then to check it by adding the numbers in the other order and by subtracting each number in turn from their answer. See also Year 2 Block B Unit 3.

Activities 7 and 8

Prior learning
Children can name common 2D shapes and 3D solids and describe their features. They can sort objects into groups according to a given criterion.

Framework objective
Visualise common 2D shapes and 3D solids; identify shapes from pictures of them in different positions and orientations; sort, make and describe shapes, referring to their properties

Vocabulary
sort, classify, property, square, rectangle, rectangular, triangle, triangular, circle, circular, pentagon, hexagon, octagon, pyramid, cube, cuboid, sphere, cone, cylinder, face, corner, edge, side, flat, curved, surface, straight, round, shape, hollow, solid, line of symmetry

Resources
Interactive activity: 2D shapes
Worksheets: 2D shapes (1) and (2)
Resource sheets: 2D shapes, Self-assessment
Classroom resources: glue, set of solid shapes (pyramid, cube, cuboid, sphere, cone and cylinder)

7 2D shapes

Open the interactive activity '2D shapes'. Invite children to drag and drop the shapes into the appropriate areas of the Carroll diagram. Ask them to name the shapes they have chosen and to describe the shapes' properties. Assess their ability to do this. Alternatively, ask them to complete the activity alone and fill in the self-assessment at the end of the activity. Next, give the children the irregular shapes cut from the resource sheet '2D shapes' and ask them to stick them onto the Carroll diagram on the worksheet '2D shapes (1)'.

Teacher support
Less confident learners: Encourage these children to point to each side as they count them. Ask them to name each shape.
More confident learners: Ask the children to think of other criteria and make up their own Carroll diagram. They then sort a second set of shapes.

Common misconception
Children do not recognise that regular and irregular shapes can have the same name if they have the same number of sides.
Give children two sets of cards (cut from the resource sheet '2D shapes'), one set showing an equilateral triangle, a regular quadrilateral, a regular pentagon and a regular octagon, and the other set showing an irregular triangle, quadrilateral, pentagon and octagon. Ask children to pair shapes with the same numbers of sides and to name them. (Point out that a square and a rectangle are different because a square has all sides equal length.)

Probing questions
- How do you know this shape is a circle?
- If a shape has six corners, how many sides will it have? Why?

Next steps
Support: Make a shape poster. Draw the shapes the children know, both regular and irregular. They cut and stick the shapes onto paper. Write labels and ask them to stick these beside the correct shapes. See also Year 2 Block B Unit 1.
Extension: Give the children a simple five-piece tangram (from the worksheet '2D shapes (2)') and ask them to use it to make and name as many different 2D shapes as they can. They should identify the shapes' properties. See also Year 2 Block B Unit 3.

BLOCK B

(8) 3D shapes

Give the children one each of the following 3D shapes: pyramid, cube, cuboid, sphere, cone, cylinder. Ask them to sort the shapes. Encourage them to sort in whichever way they wish and to explain why they made their choice. Next, ask them to describe each shape using the vocabulary of face, corner, edge, side, flat and curved. Make a note of the children who could do this and also those who need further experience. You could take a photograph of their work and annotate it. Decide whether to use the self-assessment sheet for children to record their achievements and what they need to do next.

Teacher support

Less confident learners: Prompt these children to sort the shapes into three groups: 'curved faces', 'flat faces' and 'flat and curved faces'. Ask them to name each shape.
More confident learners: Ask children to complete a simple table with the headings 'Name', 'Shape of faces', 'Number of sides' and 'Number of corners'.

Common misconception

Children cannot identify 3D shapes.
Provide children with real-life shapes (for example, a ball, dice, a tissue box) and ask them to hold each item and touch the faces, edges and vertices, saying the name of the shapes and describing their properties as they do this. Discuss what these real-life items are and how they would be used.

Probing questions

- My shape has six faces. What could it be?
- A shape has at least one square face. What could it be?
- How many things can you think of that are the same shape as a cube?

Next steps

Support: To reinforce and consolidate, work with the children to make a display of real-life 3D shapes. Make name labels (the shape names) for them to place beside each item. Ask them to place digit cards by each shape to show the number of faces, edges and corners. See also Year 1 Block B Unit 3.
Extension: As an investigation, give the children 16 interlocking cubes and ask them to make a cube, then as many different cuboids as they can. Ask them to record their results in any way they wish. See also Year 2 Block B Unit 2.

Unit 2  Securing number facts, understanding shape

Introduction

In this unit, children are encouraged to use and apply taught skills through problem solving involving the four operations in various contexts. They listen to others, ask relevant questions and follow instructions. They read and write two- and three-digit numbers, explore number sequences and recognise odd and even numbers. They visualise common 2D shapes and 3D solids, identify them from pictures in different orientations. They sort, make and describe shapes, referring to their properties. They identify reflective symmetry in shapes and draw lines of symmetry in shapes.

Framework objectives	Assessment focuses		Success criteria for Year 2	Learning outcomes
	Level 2	Level 1		
(1) Patterns				
Describe patterns and relationships involving numbers or shapes, make predictions and test these with examples	• predict what comes next in a simple number, shape or spatial pattern or sequence and give reasons for their opinions	• recognise and use a simple pattern or relationship, e.g. with support • copy and continue a simple pattern of objects, shapes or numbers	• can identify colour sequences, saying what the colour will be several places ahead of those seen • can recognise and continue simple sequences • can describe sequences	*I can describe and continue the pattern of a set of numbers or shapes.*
(2) Sammy's problem				
Solve problems involving addition, subtraction, multiplication or division in contexts of numbers, measures or pounds and pence	• select the mathematics they use in some classroom activities, e.g. with support • find a starting point, identifying key facts/relevant information • use apparatus, diagrams, role play etc to represent and clarify a problem • move between different representations of a problem e.g. a situation described in words, a diagram etc • adopt a suggested model or systematic approach • make connections and apply their knowledge to similar situations • use mathematical content from levels 1 and 2 to solve problems and investigate • choose the appropriate operation when solving addition or subtraction problems	• use mathematics as an integral part of classroom activities, e.g. with support • engage with practical mathematical activities involving sorting, counting and measuring by direct comparison • begin to understand the relevance of mathematical ideas to everyday situations by using them in role-play • solve addition/subtraction problems involving up to 10 objects, e.g. • solve problems involving 1p or £1 coins	• can work out what to do to solve a problem • can use efficient strategies to add two numbers together	*I can decide which calculations to do to solve a problem.*

Unit 2 Securing number facts, understanding shape

Framework objectives	Assessment focuses		Success criteria for Year 2	Learning outcomes
	Level 2	Level 1		
3 Number pairs				
Derive and recall all addition and subtraction facts for each number to at least 10, all pairs with totals to 20 and all pairs of multiples of 10 with totals up to 100	● use mental recall of addition and subtraction facts to 10, e.g. ● use addition/subtraction facts to 10 and place value to add or subtract multiples of 10, e.g. know 3 + 7 = 10 and use place value to derive 30 + 70 = 100	● add and subtract numbers of objects to 10 ● begin to add by counting on from the number of objects in the first set	● can recall addition and subtraction facts to 10 ● can recall number pairs for any number to 10 ● can recognise multiples of 10	*I can recall number facts for each number up to 10.* *I know which pairs of numbers make 20.*
4 Multiples of 2, 5 and 10				
Derive and recall multiplication facts for the 2-, 5- and 10-times tables and the related division facts; recognise multiples of 2, 5 and 10	● recognise sequences of numbers, including odd and even numbers, e.g. ● recognise numbers from counting in tens or twos	● order numbers to 10 ● begin to count in twos	● can count in steps of 2, 5 and 10 ● can link multiplication to repeated addition	*I know some of the number facts in the 2-, 5- and 10-times tables.* *I know that multiples of 2 are even numbers.*
5 Numbers!				
Read and write two-digit and three-digit numbers in figures and words; describe and extend number sequences and recognise odd and even numbers	● begin to understand the place value of each digit, use this to order numbers up to 100, e.g. ● know the relative size of numbers to 100 ● use zero as a place holder ● demonstrate knowledge using a range of models/ images	● read, write numbers to 10 ● perhaps with some reversal	● can read and write single-digit numbers ● can read and write two-digit numbers ● understands place value in two-digit numbers	*I can read and write two-digit and three-digit numbers.*

BLOCK B

Unit 2 Securing number facts, understanding shape

Framework objectives	Assessment focuses: Level 2	Assessment focuses: Level 1	Success criteria for Year 2	Learning outcomes
(6) Names of 2D shapes (7) Solids				
Visualise common 2D shapes and 3D solids; identify shapes from pictures of them in different positions and orientations; sort, make and describe shapes, referring to their properties	• use mathematical names for common 3D and 2D shapes, e.g. • identify 2D and 3D shapes from pictures of them in different orientations, e.g. square, triangle, hexagon, pentagon, octagon, cube, cylinder, sphere, cuboid, pyramid • describe their properties, including numbers of sides and corners, e.g. • make and talk about shapes, referring to features and properties using language such as edge, face, corner • sort 2D and 3D shapes according to a single criterion, e.g. shapes that are pentagons or shapes with a right angle • visualise frequently used 2D and 3D shapes • begin to understand the difference between shapes with two dimensions and those with three • recognise the properties that are the same even when a shape is enlarged, e.g. when comparing squares, circles, similar triangles, cubes or spheres of different sizes	• use everyday language to describe properties of 2D and 3D shapes, e.g. • sort shapes and say how they have selected them • use properties such as large, small, triangles, roll, stack • begin to refer to some features of shapes such as side and corner • begin to name the shapes they use in the context of an activity	• can recognise 2D shapes from pictures of them • can describe features of 2D shapes • can name 3D solids • can describe their features • can visualise 3D solids	*I can use a construction kit to make a model of a 3D solid that I know.*
(8) Symmetry				
Identify reflective symmetry in patterns and 2D shapes and draw lines of symmetry in shapes	• describe the properties of 2D shapes, including numbers of sides and corners, e.g. • make and talk about shapes, referring to features and properties using language such as edge, face, corner	• use everyday language to describe properties of 2D and 3D shapes, e.g. • use properties such as large, small, triangles, roll, stack • begin to refer to some features of shapes such as sides and corners	• can recognise symmetry in pictures • can recognise symmetry in regular shapes • can make symmetrical patterns	*I can make a symmetrical pattern using coloured tiles.* *I can draw a line of symmetry on a shape.*

BLOCK B

BLOCK B

Activity 1

Prior learning
Children can describe simple patterns and predict which a particular one further in the sequence would be.

Framework objective
Describe patterns and relationships involving numbers or shapes, make predictions and test these with examples

Vocabulary
explain, predict, reason, pattern, relationship

Resources
Resource sheet: Self-assessment
Classroom resources: counters in three colours

1 Patterns

Use 15 counters in three different colours to create a pattern, such as red, red, blue, yellow, red, red, blue, yellow, red... Ask the children to describe the pattern. Give them the same number of coloured counters and ask them to make a different pattern of their own. Observe how they do this, focusing on whether they really understand the idea of a pattern being a repeated sequence. Next, ask them to make some patterns where the eighth counter is blue and to record their ideas and patterns. Decide whether to use the self-assessment sheet for children to record their achievements and what they need to do next.

Teacher support
Less confident learners: Encourage these children to make sequences with ten counters of two different colours.
More confident learners: Ask children to use counters in three colours to make patterns that fulfil a specific criterion – for example, a blue counter should come after a red but not before a green. They should record their patterns on paper.

Common misconceptions
Children do not understand that a pattern repeats.
Use different coloured counters to make the first part of a simple pattern, such as red, red, blue. Repeat that part again. Ask children to place the next part of the pattern and describe what they see.

Children cannot visualise what the sixth item in a sequence will be.
Start with a simple sequence, such as red, blue, red, blue. Ask the children to say out loud the colours in order. Ask which colour will come next and encourage them to keep track on their fingers.

Probing questions
- If my pattern is red, red, blue, red..., where will the next blue counter come? How do you know?
- When will the next three blue counters come? What can help you work this out?

Next steps
Support: Give a simple criterion and ask children to make a pattern to fit it. For example: *All the even positions (second, fourth, sixth...) in the pattern are red.* Gradually increase the complexity of the criterion, such as: *Every third is blue.* See also Year 2 Block B Unit 1.
Extension: Pose a problem, such as: *My pattern is made from 24 red and blue counters. There are twice as many red counters than blue. How many red counters are there?* (16) Ask the children to predict first and then to test their prediction. See also Year 2 Block B Unit 3.

Activity 2

Prior learning

Children can solve problems involving counting, adding and subtracting, in the context of numbers, measures or money. They use efficient strategies to work out their answers.

Framework objective

Solve problems involving addition, subtraction, multiplication or division in contexts of numbers, measures or pounds and pence

Vocabulary

problem, solution, calculate, calculation, operation, inverse, answer, method, explain, predict, reason, add, subtract, multiply, divide, sum, total, difference, plus, minus

Resources

Resource sheet: Self-assessment
Classroom resources: whiteboards and pens, 1p, 2p, 5p and 10p coins

2 Sammy's problem

Write this problem on the board: *Sammy spent 28p. Sally spent 9p more than Sammy. How much did Sally spend?* Read it with the children. Discuss key facts. The children then decide what calculation is needed and work out the answer, writing it on their whiteboards with their working out. Observe how they do this. Do they recognise that an addition is required? What strategy did they use to add: counting on in ones; partitioning 9p, adding 2p to make 30p, then adding the remaining 7p to make 37p; or adding 10p and adjusting? Decide whether to use the self-assessment sheet for children to record their achievements and what they need to do next.

Teacher support

Less confident learners: Reduce the amounts in the problem to 9p and 4p and give the children pennies as a resource to help them find the answer.
More confident learners: Increase the amounts so that Sammy has 78p and Sally 29p. Observe the children's strategies for finding the answer.

Common misconception

Children cannot use efficient strategies to add two numbers together.
Concentrate on making the amount closest to 10p up to that amount by partitioning the second amount. For example: 8p + 4p = (8p + 2p) + 2p = 10p + 2p = 12p. Ask children which amount is closest to 10p and to count out the correct number of pennies. Ask them to count out the second number of coins and take the appropriate number to make the other up to 10p. Ask how many are left and add them to the ten pennies to find the total.

Probing questions

- How will you decide what to do to solve the problem?
- What strategy could you use to find the answer?
- Is there another way to find the answer?

Next steps

Support: Give the children practice at answering more simple addition and subtraction problems. Encourage them to use the bridging strategy for addition and 'counting on' for finding differences. See also Year 2 Block B Unit 1.
Extension: Give the children more experience of problems involving money and amounts involving mixed pounds and pence. Encourage them to think of efficient strategies for addition and subtraction when solving the problems and also to record their work by using jottings. See also Year 2 Block B Unit 3.

Activity 3

Prior learning
Children can recall addition and subtraction facts to 10 and pairs of multiples of 10 with totals of up to 100.

Framework objective
Derive and recall all addition and subtraction facts for each number to at least 10, all pairs with totals to 20 and all pairs of multiples of 10 with totals up to 100

Vocabulary
add, subtract, sum, total, difference, plus, minus

Resources
Resource sheets: Self-assessment, 0–20 numeral cards
Classroom resources: whiteboards and pens, counters, 20 beads or toy animals, 20cm lengths of string

3 Number pairs

Hold up a number card and ask the children to write down the number that makes it up to 20. Repeat with other numbers, giving the children about 15 seconds to write their answers. Observe how quickly and confidently they do this. Make a note of any who clearly struggle. Give the children two minutes to write pairs of multiples of 10 that make 100 and the number pairs to 20. Do they do this systematically? Make a note of those who work randomly. Decide whether to use the self-assessment sheet for children to record their achievements and what they need to do next.

Teacher support
Less confident learners: Show 20 counters. Take ten away. *How many counters are left?* Observe what children do. Do they count the counters or can they say the answer straight away? Repeat for other subtractions.
More confident learners: Say a multiple of 5. Ask the children to write the number that has to be added to make it up to 100.

Common misconception
Children are not confident recalling number pairs with a total of 10.
Encourage children to use their fingers. Ask them to show ten, put down three and say how many are left showing. Repeat for other number pairs totalling 10.

Probing questions
- Look at these multiples of 10: 10, 20, 30, 40, 50, 60, 70, 80, 90. Which pair of numbers has a total of 100? Are there any other possibilities?
- □ + ○ = 100: What two numbers could go in the box and the circle? Are there any other possibilities?

Next steps
Support: Focus on pairs totalling 20. Use beads or toy animals to work out the pairs. Ask real-life problems, such as: *I had 20cm of string and cut off 12cm. How much have I got left?* Carry out the activity. See also Year 2 Block B Unit 1.
Extension: Focus on pairs of multiples of 5 to 100. Ask the children to tell you how their knowledge of other number pairs can help with this. See also Year 2 Block B Unit 3.

Activity 4

Prior learning
Children can count in steps of 2, 5 and 10.

Framework objective
Derive and recall multiplication facts for the 2-, 5- and 10-times tables and the related division facts; recognise multiples of 2, 5 and 10

Vocabulary
add, multiply, divide, inverse

Resources
Worksheet: Multiples of 2, 5 and 10
Resource sheets: 0–50 number lines, 100-square

4 Multiples of 2, 5 and 10

Together, count in twos to 20 and back again. Repeat for fives and tens. Ask for random times-tables facts, encouraging the children to use their fingers to count on each step if they cannot recall a fact instantly. Repeat for division by asking questions such as: *What is 20 divided by 5*? Ask the children to count on in fives to 20. Discuss what is special about a multiple of 2 (even), then multiples of 5 (ends in 5 or zero) and multiples of 10 (ends in zero). Give the children the worksheet 'Multiples of 2, 5 and 10' and ask them to complete it. (Note: numbers might belong in more than one circle.)

Teacher support
Less confident learners: Focus on 10-times table facts. Ask the children to count in tens, using their fingers. Stop at various points, asking them how many fingers they are showing and how many that is in tens.
More confident learners: Practise instant recall of 2-, 5- and 10-times table facts.

Common misconceptions
Children cannot count in steps of 2, 5 and 10.
Provide a number line and ask children to begin at zero and draw a line to 2, then 4, 6 (and so on), saying aloud the number they land on each time. Then ask them to count in twos again, without the line. Repeat for fives. Use a 100-square for the tens.

Children do not link counting in equal steps to the operation of multiplication.
Draw some dots and repeated addition and multiplication sentences. Ask the child to match them. For example:

1 + 1

1 × 2

Probing questions
- What are the missing numbers in these number sentences: □ × 2 = 18, 10 × □ = 30, □ × ○ = 20. How do you know?
- How can you use 5 × 10 = 50 to work out 5 × 11?
- How do you know if a number is a multiple of 5?

Next steps
Support: Focus on counting in steps of 2, 5 and 10, using apparatus first, and then number lines and a 100-square, and finally counting by memory. Link to repeated addition and the times-tables facts. See also Year 2 Block B Unit 1.
Extension: Extend to learning 4-times table multiplication and division facts. Discuss the relationship with the 2-times table. See Year 2 Block B Unit 3.

Activity 5

Prior learning
Children can read and write single-digit and two-digit numbers in figures and words.

Framework objective
Read and write two-digit and three-digit numbers in figures and words; describe and extend number sequences and recognise odd and even numbers

Vocabulary
one, two, three, four, five, six, seven, eight, nine, ten, eleven, twelve, thirteen, fourteen, fifteen, sixteen, seventeen, eighteen, nineteen, twenty, thirty, forty, fifty, sixty, seventy, eighty, ninety, hundred

Resources
Resource sheets: Self-assessment, Place value arrow cards, 0–10 digit cards
Classroom resources: whiteboards and pens, place value equipment

5 Numbers!

Ask the children to write the number 8 as a figure and as a word on their whiteboards and then follow further instructions. For example: *Add 1. Add 40. Take away 5. What number do you have?* Each time, ask the children to write their answer in figures and words. Repeat, this time starting with 245, and say: *Add 100. Take away 50. What do you have?* Observe the children as they do this, making a note of any who struggle with a view to working with them later. Decide whether to use the self-assessment sheet for children to record their achievements and what they need to do next.

Teacher support
Less confident learners: Call out two-digit numbers for these children to write down. Gradually build in simple instructions, such as: *Write the number that is 1 more, 10 less.*
More confident learners: Extend to four-digit numbers and give more complex instructions.

Common misconceptions
Children reverse teens numbers.
Show children place value arrow cards for the numbers they confuse (for example, 13 and 31), so that they can compare the numbers and identify the correct number before writing it.

Children cannot write two-digit numbers.
Provide place value arrow cards for two-digit numbers to 30. Together make a number (for example, 24). Ask children to say the numbers that make it (20 and 4), then the whole number and finally ask them to write it. Repeat several times and then ask them to write the numbers without the prompts.

Probing questions
- Which of these numbers says 34? How do you know?
- How are these numbers the same/different?
- Name all the three-digit numbers you can make with 3, 4 and 5.

Next steps
Support: Make two-digit numbers with place value arrow cards. Ask the children to use place value equipment to make the numbers shown so that they can visualise how many each is worth. See also Year 2 Block A Unit 2.
Extension: Show three digit cards. Ask the children to write all the three-digit numbers they can make with them. Then ask them to partition each number. For example, for cards 4, 6 and 7, children might write 400 + 60 + 7 = 467. See also Year 2 Block A Unit 3.

Activities 6 and 7

Prior learning
Children can recognise and name common 2D shapes from pictures of them and describe their features.

Framework objective
Visualise common 2D shapes and 3D solids; identify shapes from pictures of them in different positions and orientations; sort, make and describe shapes, referring to their properties

Vocabulary
sort, classify, property, square, rectangle, rectangular, triangle, triangular, circle, circular, pentagon, hexagon, octagon, pyramid, cube, cuboid, sphere, cone, cylinder, face, corner, edge, side, flat, curved, surface, straight, round, shape, hollow, solid, line of symmetry

Resources
Interactive activity: Names of 2D shapes
Resource sheet: Self-assessment
Classroom resources: pictures of circles, triangles, squares, rectangles, pentagons, hexagons and octagons, Plasticine®, construction equipment (such as Clixi®)

6 Names of 2D shapes

Show the children pictures of these shapes: circle, triangle, square, rectangle, pentagon, hexagon and octagon. Ask them to name the shapes and describe their properties. Reveal the interactive activity 'Names of 2D shapes'. Ask the children to play the game in pairs or small groups as if playing a normal game of dominoes but for shapes rather than dots. Observe them as they do this and make a note of any who are not able to make matches.

Teacher support
Less confident learners: Let these children use talk partners to discuss moves. Provide flat shapes to further support their understanding.
More confident learners: Encourage these children to think of a way to record their work, giving them the opportunity to practise drawing shapes and writing names.

Common misconceptions
Children have difficulty recognising 2D shapes.
Show children a 2D shape and ask them to trace around it with a finger, saying its name. Hide the shape and ask them to draw it on paper from memory.

Children have difficulty matching the shape name with the shape.
Show shape names on cards and describe each without using the word. The child needs to draw the shape, say the name and place the word with their drawing.

Probing questions
- Why can't this shape be a square?
- What is the same/different about these shapes?

Next steps
Support: To reinforce and consolidate, give these children pictures of shapes. They should describe them in terms of their properties without using their actual names for a partner to guess. See also Year 2 Block B Unit 1.
Extension: Ask the children to think of irregular versions of the shapes they have been working with and draw a selection. Give criteria such as 'there must be one right angle', 'two lines of symmetry'. See also Year 2 Block B Unit 3.

BLOCK B

7 Solids

Give the children some Plasticine® and ask them to make each of these shapes: sphere, cube, cuboid, cylinder and pyramid, in that order. It might help them to begin with a sphere and shape the next one from that by flattening and rounding as appropriate. As they make each shape, ask them to name it. Assess their ability to do this. Can they visualise the shape that they are making? Decide whether to use the self-assessment sheet for children to record their achievements and what they need to do next.

Teacher support

Less confident learners: Give these children the actual shapes to look at to support their understanding as they do the activity.
More confident learners: Encourage these children to sort their shapes according to criteria that they make up (for example, round/not round or has/does not have six faces).

Common misconception

Children have difficulty recognising properties of a 3D shape.
Provide a collection of 2D and 3D shapes. Give each child a solid shape and ask them to find a 2D shape that is the same shape as one of the faces of the solid shape. Ask children to check one another's shapes and to explain whether they are correct or not. Are there any other 2D shapes that they could have chosen?

Probing questions

- How do you know this shape is a cylinder?
- How do you know this shape isn't a cone?
- Imagine a cube. Three faces are red, the rest are blue. How many are blue?

Next steps

Support: To reinforce and consolidate, give the children construction equipment (such as Clixi®) and ask them to make a cube, cuboid and a pyramid. Let them see the actual shapes as a guide. See also Year 2 Block B Unit 1.
Extension: Give the children some Plasticine®. Ask them to make pyramids with different bases, and then to draw the faces of each pyramid. What do they notice about the relationship between the number of sides of the base and the number of triangular faces? See also Year 2 Block B Unit 3.

Activity 8

Prior learning
Children can recognise symmetry in pictures (for example, butterflies).

Framework objective
Identify reflective symmetry in patterns and 2D shapes and draw lines of symmetry in shapes

Vocabulary
line of symmetry

Resources
Worksheet: Symmetry
Resource sheet: 2D shapes
Classroom resources: counters of different colours

8 Symmetry

Ask the children to draw a line down the middle of a piece of paper. Give them coloured counters, and ask them to arrange them on the paper so that they make a symmetrical pattern. Check that the counters on one side of the line are the same as those on the other. Ask them to record their patterns on paper and to draw on the line of symmetry.

Teacher support
Less confident learners: Make a simple pattern (using only one colour) on one side of the line on the paper. The children complete it by placing counters appropriately on the other side of the line.
More confident learners: Encourage these children to make more complicated patterns.

Common misconceptions
Children cannot identify lines of symmetry in 2D shapes.
Ask children to fold a rectangular piece of paper in half and to describe what has happened (one half is the same as the other). Repeat for drawings of different shapes that can be halved.

Children cannot make symmetrical patterns.
Build this up gradually using practical apparatus and appropriate ICT programs, then by asking children to colour their own symmetrical patterns.

Probing questions
- How many lines of symmetry does this shape have?
- Can you explain why a square has four lines of symmetry but a rectangle only has two?
- My shape has three lines of symmetry. What could it be?

Next steps
Support: To reinforce, provide cut-out shapes (from the resource sheet '2D shapes'), some of which have lines of symmetry and some of which don't. The children examine them and decide which don't have any lines of symmetry, then fold the shapes in half to check. See also Year 1 Block B Unit 2.
Extension: Provide the worksheet 'Symmetry'. The first few shapes have been folded in half once, the rest twice. Ask children to imagine opening them up, and then draw what they think they would look like. See also Year 3 Block B Unit 2.

Unit 3 Securing number facts, understanding shape

Introduction

Children are encouraged to use and apply taught skills and tell real or imagined stories (using conventions of familiar story language) to describe number problems. They make use of addition and subtraction facts, multiples of 2, 5 and 10 and doubles and halves to estimate and check answers to calculations and problems involving the four operations in different contexts. They know most of their multiplication facts for 2-, 5- and 10-times tables and corresponding divisions. They visualise common 2D shapes and 3D solids and identify them from pictures in different orientations. They sort, make and describe shapes, referring to their properties. Threaded throughout the unit are the 'using and applying' objectives in a variety of contexts.

Framework objectives	Assessment focuses		Success criteria for Year 2	Learning outcomes
	Level 2	Level 1		
(1) Pattern sequences				
Describe patterns and relationships involving numbers or shapes; make predictions and test these with examples	• predict what comes next in a simple number, shape or spatial pattern or sequence and give reasons for their opinions	• recognise and use a simple pattern or relationship, e.g. with support • copy and continue a simple pattern of objects, shapes or numbers	• can describe patterns and relationships involving numbers or shapes • can make sequences with shapes and numbers	*I can describe and continue the pattern of a set of numbers or shapes.*
(2) Problem solving				
Solve problems involving addition, subtraction, multiplication or division in contexts of numbers, measures or pounds and pence	• choose the appropriate operation when solving addition and subtraction problems • use repeated addition to solve multiplication problems • begin to use repeated subtraction or sharing equally to solve division problems • solve number problems involving money and measures, e.g. • add/subtract two-digit and single-digit numbers, bridging tens where necessary, in contexts using units such as pence, pounds, centimetres	• solve addition/subtraction problems involving up to ten objects, e.g. • solve measuring problems such as 'How many balance with...' • solve problems involving 1p or £1 coins	• can solve problems involving adding, subtracting, doubling or halving, simple multiplication and division, in the context of numbers, measures or money	*I can decide which calculations are needed to solve a two-step word problem.*

Framework objectives	Assessment focuses		Success criteria for Year 2	Learning outcomes
	Level 2	Level 1		
③ Solve it				
Derive and recall all addition and subtraction facts for each number to at least 10, all pairs with totals to 20 and all pairs of multiples of 10 with totals up to 100	• use mental recall of addition and subtraction facts to 10 e.g. • use addition/subtraction facts to 10 and place value to add or subtract multiples of 10, e.g. know 3 + 7 = 10 and use place value to derive 30 + 70 = 100	• add and subtract numbers of objects to 10 • begin to add by counting on from the number of objects in the first set	• can recall addition and subtraction facts to 10 • can recall doubles of all numbers to 10 • can recall addition and subtraction facts of multiples of 10	*I know which pairs of numbers make 20.* *I know all the pairs of multiples of 10 that make 100.*
④ Doubles and halves				
Understand that halving is the inverse of doubling and derive and recall doubles of all numbers to 20, and the corresponding halves	• understand halving as a way of 'undoing' doubling and vice versa • use mental calculation strategies to solve number problems including those involving money and measures, e.g. • recall doubles to 10 + 10 and other significant doubles, e.g. double 50p is 100p or £1 • use knowledge of doubles to 10 + 10 to derive corresponding halves	• begin to know some addition facts, e.g. • doubles of numbers to double 5	• can double numbers to 20 and find their corresponding halves in the context of numbers, measures or money	*I know the doubles of all the numbers up to 20.*
⑤ Times-tables facts				
Derive and recall multiplication facts for the 2-, 5- and 10-times tables and the related division facts; recognise multiples of 2, 5 and 10	• recognise sequences of numbers, including odd and even numbers, e.g. • recognise numbers from counting in tens or twos	• order numbers to 10 • begin to count in twos	• can recognise multiples of 2, 5 and 10 • can recognise that counting in equal steps links to the operation of multiplication	*I know my 2-, 5- and 10-times tables and can work out the division facts that go with them.* *I can tell if a number is a multiple of 2, 5 or 10.*
⑥ Match up!				
Use knowledge of number facts and operations to estimate and check answers to calculations	• use mental recall of addition and subtraction facts to 10 e.g. • use addition/subtraction facts to 10 and place value to add or subtract multiples of 10, e.g. know 3 + 7 = 10 and use place value to derive 30 + 70 = 100	• add or subtract numbers of objects to 10 • begin to add by counting on from the number of objects in the first set	• can add or subtract two two-digit numbers • can check using the inverse operation	*I can check answers to calculations involving doubling by halving the answer.*

BLOCK B

Unit 3 Securing number facts, understanding shape

Framework objectives	Assessment focuses		Success criteria for Year 2	Learning outcomes
	Level 2	Level 1		
(7) Sorting 2D shapes (8) From picture to 3D				
Visualise common 2D shapes and 3D solids; identify shapes from pictures of them in different positions and orientations; sort, make and describe shapes, referring to their properties	• use mathematical names for common 3D and 2D shapes, e.g. • identify 2D and 3D shapes from pictures of them in different orientations, e.g. square, triangle, hexagon, pentagon, octagon, cube, cylinder, sphere, cuboid, pyramid • describe their properties, including numbers of sides and corners, e.g. • make and talk about shapes referring to features and properties using language such as edge, face, corner • sort 2D and 3D shapes according to a single criterion, e.g. shapes that are pentagons or shapes with a right angle • visualise frequently used 2D and 3D shapes • begin to understand the difference between shapes with two dimensions and those with three • recognise the properties that are the same even when a shape is enlarged, e.g. when comparing squares, circles, similar triangles, cubes or spheres of different sizes	• use everyday language to describe properties of 2D and 3D shapes, e.g. • sort shapes and say how they have selected them • use properties such as large, small, triangles, roll, stack • begin to refer to some features of shapes such as sides and corners • begin to name the shapes they use in the context of an activity	• can name 2D and 3D shapes • can describe the features of 2D and 3D shapes • can sort 2D and 3D shapes into groups according to a given criterion • can recognise 3D shapes in real life	*I can match familiar solids to their pictures.*

BLOCK B

Activity 1

Prior learning

Children can describe simple patterns and relationships involving numbers or shapes.

Framework objective

Describe patterns and relationships involving numbers or shapes, make predictions and test these with examples

Vocabulary

explain, predict, reason, pattern, relationship

Resources

Resource sheets: Self-assessment, 0–50 number lines
Classroom resources: 2D and 3D shapes (at least 12 shapes for each child, including three different shapes), counters, whiteboards and pens

1 Pattern sequences

Ask the children to use the shapes to make repeating patterns. Once they have each made a pattern, ask them to describe it and then to predict what the 15th shape in their sequence will be. Extend the sequence to check. Repeat for numbers, counting in steps of 5 or 10 from different starting numbers. Ask the children to predict the next few numbers in the sequence by looking at the pattern of the units and tens digits (for example, for steps of 5, alternate units digits will be the same). Encourage the children to record their sequences. Decide whether to use the self-assessment sheet for children to record their achievements and what they need to do next.

Teacher support

Less confident learners: Ask the children to use just two shapes to create a simple pattern. Provide number lines to support their counting in steps.
More confident learners: Ask: *What will the 20th shape be? How do you know? Count in steps of 4 or 3.*

Common misconceptions

Children cannot make a sequence.
Use different-coloured counters to make a simple sequence, such as 'red, blue, red, blue', and ask children to continue it. Once they have done this, start a more complicated sequence for them to continue. Ask them to explain how the pattern works.

Children cannot make a sequence with numbers.
Begin a simple sequence, such as '1, 2, 1, 2...', and ask children to continue it. Write a sequence that is slightly more complicated and ask children to continue it. Invite them to explain the pattern, and then to make up their own patterns.

Probing questions

- If my sequence is 'circle, square, square, triangle', what would the 11th shape be? How do you know?
- A number sequence starts '12, 17, 22, 27'. What would the tenth number be? How do you know?

Next steps

Support: Work with these children to make simple shape or number sequences. Ask them to use three different types of shapes to make a sequence. See also Year 2 Block B Unit 2.
Extension: Show the start of different sequences and ask the children to predict the 10th and 13th shape or number. Encourage them to work it out from the pattern. See also Year 3 Block B Unit 1.

Activity 2

Prior learning
Children can solve problems involving adding, subtracting, doubling or halving, simple multiplication and division, in the context of numbers, measures or money.

Framework objective
Solve problems involving addition, subtraction, multiplication or division in contexts of numbers, measures or pounds and pence

Vocabulary
problem, solution, calculate, calculation, operation, inverse, answer, method, explain, predict, reason, add, subtract, multiply, divide, sum, total, difference, plus, minus

Resources
Worksheet: Problem solving
Classroom resources: counters, counting objects

2 Problem solving

Give each child the worksheet 'Problem solving'. This contains one- and two-step problems involving the four operations. At the end of the worksheet children have to make up their own word problems involving given calculations. Talk through each problem, asking the children what it is about, what information they need and which operation is required to solve it. Provide support for reading as necessary and have available counting objects such as counters for children to use if they need to.

Teacher support
Less confident learners: Use the questions on the worksheet 'Problem solving' but simplify the numbers so that, for example, numbers are less than 20, the money is to £1 and prices are in multiples of 10p, and the multiplications are by 2 or 5.
More confident learners: Create some simple word problems based on those on the worksheet 'Problem solving', but use higher numbers.

Common misconception
Children cannot identify what they need to do to solve a word problem.
Rephrase the problem or discuss the vocabulary used in the problem. Ask children to circle the relevant parts of the problem and to write the symbols that match each part. Demonstrate how to write a number sentence for the problem and where each part of it comes from.

Probing questions
- What is the important information?
- How do you know what to do to find the answer?
- How can you solve this problem using a number line?

Next steps
Support: Ask similar problems to those on the worksheet 'Problem solving'. Provide suitable equipment and work through each step of a problem with the children, questioning appropriately to guide them through the task. See also Year 2 Block B Unit 2.
Extension: Extend to problems that involve explaining how the children know something. For example: *This number line shows a sum. What is that sum? How do you know?* See also Year 3 Block B Unit 1.

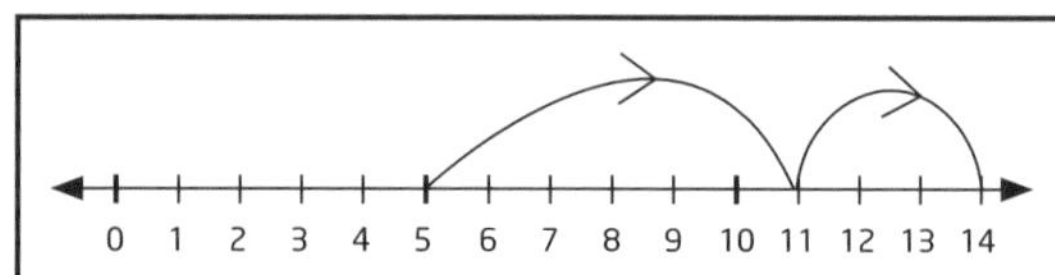

Activity 3

Prior learning
Children can recall addition and subtraction facts to ten and doubles of all numbers to at least ten.

Framework objective

Derive and recall all addition and subtraction facts for each number to at least 10, all pairs with totals to 20 and all pairs of multiples of 10 with totals up to 100

Vocabulary

add, subtract, sum, total, difference, plus, minus

Resources

Worksheet: Solve it
Classroom resources: counters in different colours, pennies and pound coins

Solve it

Pose this problem: *I had eight balloons. Some were red and the others were blue. How many of each colour could I have?* Ask the children to write number sentences to show all the possibilities. Pose this problem: *I had eight balloons and some burst. How many could I have left?* Ask the children to write number sentences to show all possibilities. Explain the worksheet 'Solve it'. Stress that the children are to write all the possible answers. Sit with individuals to observe their methods, and ask questions such as: *How do you know whether to add or subtract?*

Teacher support

Less confident learners: Provide counters in different colours to represent the numbers of items on the worksheet 'Solve it'.
More confident learners: Ask additional questions to assess children's ability to tell you pairs of numbers to 20 and multiples of 10 to 100.

Common misconception

Children are not confident recalling addition and subtraction facts for each number to at least 10.
Focus on each number to 10 in turn. For example, for 7: place seven counters in a row and ask children to move one counter away from the row and write the number sentences this illustrates: 6 + 1 = 7 and 7 - 1 = 6. Encourage children to find all the possible ways that the counters can be grouped and write the number sentences. These could be made into posters for children to refer to in the classroom.

Probing questions

- Look at this number sentence: $9 - x = y$. What could the two missing numbers be? What else?
- Can you show me all the subtraction pairs with numbers less than 10 that leave 3? How do you know you have told me them all?

Next steps

Support: Focus on pairs totalling 10. Give the children pennies and pound coins and ask real-life problems, such as: *I had 10p and bought two different sweets. How much could they each have cost?* See also Year 2 Block B Unit 2.
Extension: Encourage the children to make up problems that involve using number pairs of multiples of 10 to 100 and number facts to 20, then 30, 40 and 50. See also Year 3 Block B Unit 1.

BLOCK B

Activity 4

Prior learning

Children can double numbers to 20 and find their corresponding halves in the context of numbers, measures or money.

Framework objective

Understand that halving is the inverse of doubling and derive and recall doubles of all numbers to 20, and the corresponding halves

Vocabulary

add, multiply, inverse, halve, halved, double, doubled

Resources

Resource sheets: Doubles and halves, 1–20 numeral cards, 20–40 numeral cards (even numbers only)
Classroom resources: different-coloured counters, Plasticine®, coins, beads and/or counters

4 Doubles and halves

Give each pair of children a spinner from the resource sheet 'Doubles and halves' and the number cards. They place the 1–20 cards and the 20–40 cards in separate shuffled piles, face down. The first player spins the spinner. If the instruction is to halve, they halve the top number on the 20–40 pile. If the instruction is to double, they double the top number on the 1–20 pile. If the player is correct, they keep that card to one side in their 'winnings' pile. If the player is incorrect or spins 'miss a go', they wait until their next turn. The winner is the player with the most cards in their winnings pile.

Teacher support

Less confident learners: Double numbers to 10 and find the corresponding halves, using counters. Ask the children to describe what they do.
More confident learners: Double two-digit multiples of 10 and find the corresponding halves and also multiples of 100 to 1000.

Common misconception

Children do not appreciate that halves have to be exactly the same size.
Ask children to make 'chocolate bars' out of Plasticine®, and ask them to give half a bar to someone else. Ask children to make 12 'chocolate truffles' out of Plasticine® and to give half of them to a partner. Again, emphasise that there should be the same number in each share for them to be halves.

Probing questions

- Double 12 is 24. Can you explain how you can use this fact to say what half of 24 is?
- I'm thinking of a number. I've halved it and the answer is 45. What number was I thinking of? Explain how you know.

Next steps

Support: Focus on doubles numbers to 10 and their corresponding halves. Use money, beads and counters to double and halve, linking the two as inverse operations. Pose real-life problems, such as: *I had 18 books. My friend had half that number. How many did she have?* See also Year 2 Block B Unit 1.
Extension: Focus on numbers to 50. Pose questions such as: *I'm thinking of a number. I've halved it and the answer is 19. What number was I thinking of?* Ask the children to explain how they know. See also Year 3 Block B Unit 1.

Activity 5

Prior learning
Children can recognise multiples of 2, 5 and 10.

Framework objective
Derive and recall multiplication facts for the 2-, 5- and 10-times tables and the related division facts; recognise multiples of 2, 5 and 10

Vocabulary
add, multiply, divide, inverse

Resources
Resource sheets: Self-assessment, 0–20 number lines, 100-square
Classroom resources: whiteboards and pens

5 Times-tables facts

Give the children a mental maths test to see how quickly they can recall the facts for the 2-, 5- and 10-times tables. Call out a mixture of about 20 times-tables facts. The children write their answers on their whiteboards. Once you have done this, ask some word problems in which children need to use these facts, such as: *Sita had 40 cakes. She divided them equally into five boxes. How many cakes were in each box?* Decide whether to use the self-assessment sheet for children to record their achievements and what they need to do next.

Teacher support
Less confident learners: Focus on 10-times table facts and corresponding divisions.
More confident learners: Extend to 3-times table facts and corresponding divisions.

Common misconception
Children cannot count in steps of 2, 5 or 10.
Provide 0–20 number lines. Ask children to begin at zero and draw a line to 2, then to 4, to 6..., saying aloud the number they land on each time. Repeat this without the number line. Repeat for fives. Use a 100-square for tens.

Probing questions
- Sam worked this out: 9 × 5 = 45. How he could have worked out his answer? Is there another way?
- Sasha worked out that 40 ÷ 5 = 8. How could she have worked out her answer?

Next steps
Support: Focus on 10-times table facts using a 10 × 10 array. The children build up from 10 × 1 to 10 × 10 by running their fingers across the rows of dots and saying the appropriate fact. Repeat this for twos and fives using arrays of 20 and 50 dots as appropriate. See also Year 2 Block B Unit 2.
Extension: Extend to learning the 3-times table and, by doubling, link this to the 6-times table. See also Year 2 Block E Unit 3.

Prior learning

Children can use informal written methods to add or subtract two two-digit numbers. They can check using the inverse operation.

Framework objective

Use knowledge of number facts and operations to estimate and check answers to calculations

Vocabulary

solution, calculate, calculation, operation, inverse, answer, method, explain, predict, reason, add, subtract, multiply, divide, sum, total, difference, plus, minus, halve, halved, double, doubled

Resources

Interactive activity: Match up!
Resource sheets: 0-20 number lines, 0-10 digit cards
Classroom resources: whiteboards and pens, counters

6 Match up!

Reveal the interactive activity 'Match up!'. Point to a calculation in the first list. Ask the children to identify the calculation in the second list which they would use to check the first calculation. They write it on their whiteboards and hold it up when you say *Show me*. Check the answers shown. Ask the children to explain how they knew which calculation to use. Invite a volunteer to come to the screen and drag the arrow across so that the two matching calculations are linked. Repeat for the other calculations or ask the children to work through the activity individually on the computer (or interactive whiteboard).

Teacher support

Less confident learners: These children should concentrate on the addition inversions and those for doubling and halving.
More confident learners: Ask these children to list all the related calculations. For example, for 44 + 36 = 80 they should write 80 - 36 = 44, 36 + 44 = 80 and 80 - 44 = 36.

Common misconceptions

Children are not confident that addition can be done in any order.
Model 6 + 7 and 7 + 6, using counters, and write the number sentences.

Children cannot make the link between addition and subtraction.
Use a 0-20 number line. Ask children to point to 6 and then jump on 7. Where did they land? Use counters to confirm. Next count back seven places on the number line. Do they land on the starting number? Take away seven counters. Are there six left? Write 6 + 7 = 13 and 13 - 7 = 6.

Probing questions

- How can I check that double 24 is 48?
- How can I check that 73 - 45 = 28 is correct? Is there another way?

Next steps

Support: Focus on using the number line to add and then subtract the number added, to reinforce the concept that subtraction 'undoes' addition. Repeat for doubling and halving, and simple multiplications and divisions. Write the associated number sentences each time and draw an inversion loop. See also Year 2 Block B Unit 1.
Extension: Ask these children to use digit cards to make a two-digit number and multiply it by 2 and then by 5, and to check each multiplication by division. See also Year 3 Block B Unit 1.

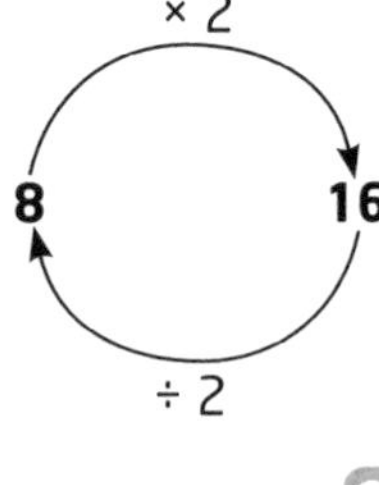

Activities  and 8

Prior learning
Children can name and describe 2D shapes and 3D solids. They can sort objects into groups according to a given criterion.

Framework objective
Visualise common 2D shapes and 3D solids; identify shapes from pictures of them in different positions and orientations; sort, make and describe shapes, referring to their properties

Vocabulary
sort, classify, property, square, rectangle, rectangular, triangle, triangular, circle, circular, pentagon, hexagon, octagon, pyramid, cube, cuboid, sphere, spherical, cone, cylinder, face, corner, edge, side, flat, curved, surface, straight, round, shape, hollow, solid, line of symmetry

Resources
Interactive activity: Sorting 2D shapes
Worksheet: From picture to 3D
Classroom resources: squared paper, sets of shapes: pyramid, cube, cuboid, sphere, cone and cylinder (a set each), real-life shape items (ball, dice etc)

7 Sorting 2D shapes

Display the interactive activity 'Sorting 2D shapes'. Invite children to drag and drop the shapes into the appropriate areas of the Carroll diagram. Ask them to name the shapes they have chosen and to describe their properties. Assess their ability to do this, making a note of those who are successful and highlighting those who will need further consolidation. Ask them to make as many shapes as they can by colouring four squares on their squared paper with sides touching, such as:

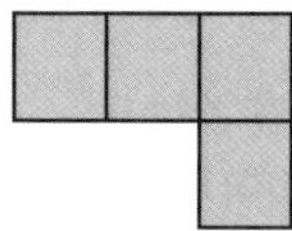

Ask the children to name their shapes. (Four are possible: oblong (rectangle), square, hexagon and octagon.)

Teacher support
Less confident learners: When working with the interactive activity, give the children a selection of shapes to sort into those with and without right angles.
More confident learners: Ask children to make two-criteria Carroll diagrams with one criterion relating to right angles and the other of their own choice.

Common misconception
Children have difficulty recognising right angles.
Help children to make a right-angle measurer by folding a piece of paper in half twice. Encourage them to slip the corner of their folded paper into corners of shapes to identify right angles. Discuss how squares and rectangles all have right angles, and ask children to find examples of right angles in the classroom.

Probing questions
- What is the same about these two shapes?
- What is different about these two shapes?
- I am showing you part of a shape. What could it be?

Next steps
Support: Work with the children to sort shapes according to different criteria. Encourage them to make up their own criteria. See also Year 2 Block B Unit 2.
Extension: Give the children opportunities to make their own Carroll diagrams with two criteria to sort all the Year 2 2D shapes. See also Year 3 Block B Unit 1.

BLOCK B

8 From picture to 3D

Show the 3D shapes that the children have experienced during the course of the lessons covered in this block. Ask the children to tell a partner the name of each shape and describe their properties. Encourage them to include the number of faces, edges and corners and the name(s) of the faces. Sit with pairs of children so that you can observe, listen and make assessment notes. Next, give the children the worksheet 'From picture to 3D' and ask them to label each picture of a real-life item with its 3D shape name.

Teacher support

Less confident learners: Give these children the appropriate 3D shapes so that they can use these to match with the pictures.
More confident learners: Encourage these children to write down the properties of the shapes of each real-life object.

Common misconceptions

Children cannot identify 3D shapes.
Provide the children with real-life shapes (for example, ball, dice, tissue box) and ask them to hold each item and touch the faces, edges and vertices, saying the name of the shapes as they do this. Discuss what these real-life items are and how they would be used.

Children cannot link the shapes of the faces of 3D shapes with their 2D equivalents.
Give the children pictures of a square and rectangle and ask them to identify these on a cuboid. Repeat with a square and triangle for a pyramid and then for other shapes.

Probing questions

- Can you tell me real-life things that are the same shape as this cube?
- How do you know they are?
- How many things can you think of that are spherical?

Next steps

Support: To reinforce and consolidate, collect pictures of real-life 3D shapes from catalogues or the internet. Make a poster by cutting and sticking these in like groups, then labelling them with their shape names. See also Year 2 Block B Unit 2.
Extension: You could give the support activity to these children but expect them to work independently and to describe the features of the shapes on their posters. See also Year 3 Block B Unit 1.

Periodic assessment

These activities can be used at the end of this block to assess those children that you think have achieved the objectives.

Number facts to ten

Framework objective

Derive and recall all addition and subtraction facts for each number to at least 10, all pairs with totals to 20 and all pairs of multiples of 10 with totals up to 100

Learning outcomes

- I can recall number facts for each number up to 10.
- I know which pairs of numbers make 20.
- I know all the pairs of multiples of 10 that make 100.

1. Write this on the board: ○ + □ = 5. Give the children one minute to write as many correct number sentences as they can. Call out some numbers and ask the children to write the number that pairs with them to make 10.
2. Ask the children to make a list of all the number pairs they can for 20. Observe how they do this: are they systematic? Write on the board the multiples of 10 to 100. Invite the children to find the pairs that total 100 and write them in a number sentence.
3. Write the numbers 1 to 10 on the board. Ask the children to make a list of all the number pairs they know for each number. Observe how they do this. Call out a number and ask the children to write the number that pairs with it to make 20. Decide whether to use the self-assessment sheet for the children to record their achievements and next steps.

2D and 3D shapes

Framework objective

Visualise common 2D shapes and 3D solids; identify shapes from pictures of them in different positions and orientations; sort, make and describe shapes, referring to their properties

Learning outcomes

- I can look at pictures of 2D shapes and name them.
- I can use a construction kit to make a model of a 3D solid that I know.
- I can match familiar solids to their pictures.

1. 2D shapes: Give each child the worksheet '2D and 3D shapes (1)'. Ask them to tick the hexagons, draw a ring around the octagons and then write the names of the remaining shapes. **3D shapes:** Give each child the worksheet '2D and 3D shapes (2)' and ask them to complete it.

2. 2D shapes: Give the children a piece of A3 paper and ask them to make a shape poster showing a circle, triangle, square, rectangle, pentagon, hexagon and octagon. Encourage them to include both regular and irregular shapes where appropriate. **3D shapes:** Give each child the worksheet '2D and 3D shapes (3)'. Describe a 3D shape that is on the worksheet. Say the number and shape of faces and the number of its edges and corners. Children write the number of the shape beside its picture. For example, you say: *Shape number one has no edges or corners, and only one face*, and the children write '1' beside the sphere.

3. 2D shapes: Give each child a copy of the worksheet '2D and 3D shapes (4)'. Show them how to use the decision tree diagram. They read each description, look at the shapes provided above and then write the correct labels in the empty boxes. **3D shapes:** Give each child a set of picture cards from the resource sheet '2D and 3D shapes (5)'. Explain that you are going to describe a 3D shape from the resource sheet. Say the number and shape of faces and the number of its edges and corners. The children look at the picture cards and hold up the one that matches your description.

Name Date

BLOCK B

2D and 3D shapes (1)

- Tick the hexagons.
- Draw a ring around the octagons.

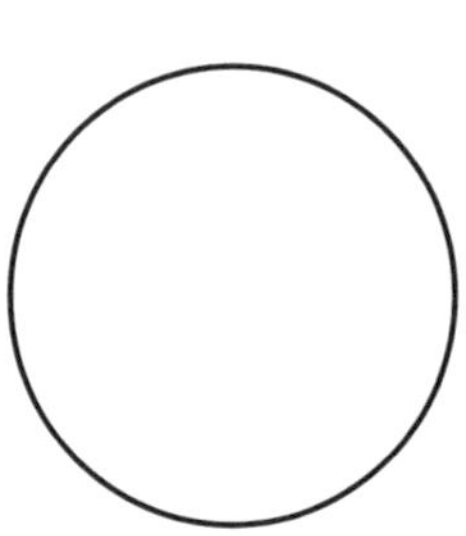
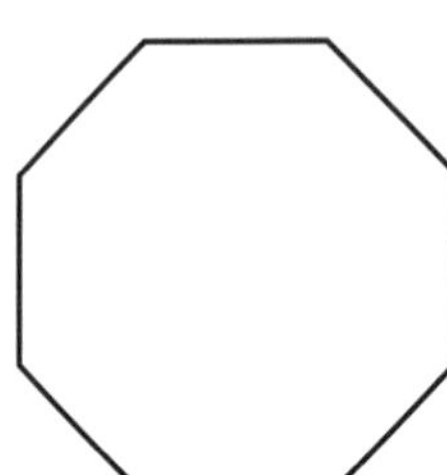
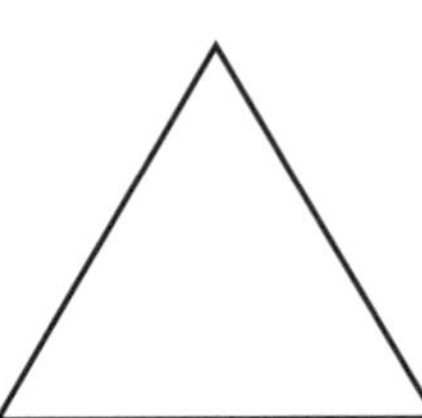
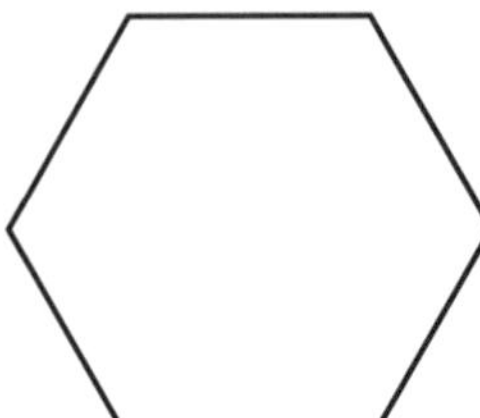
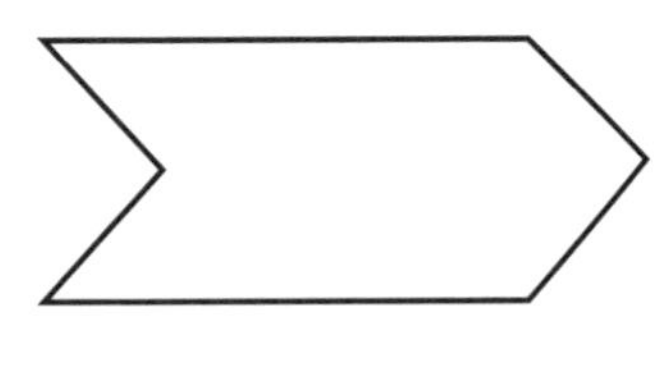
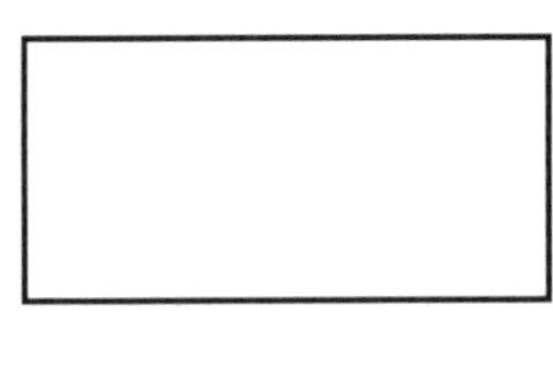
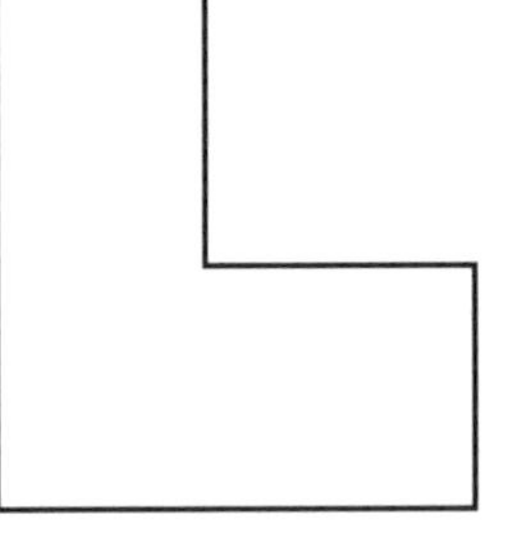
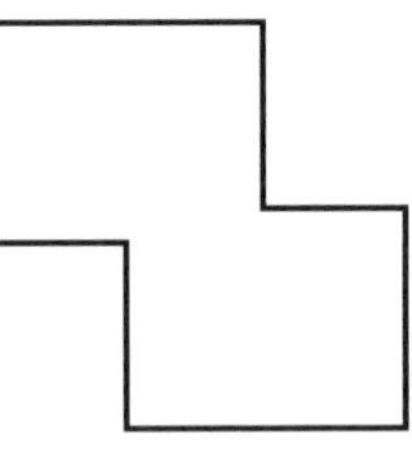
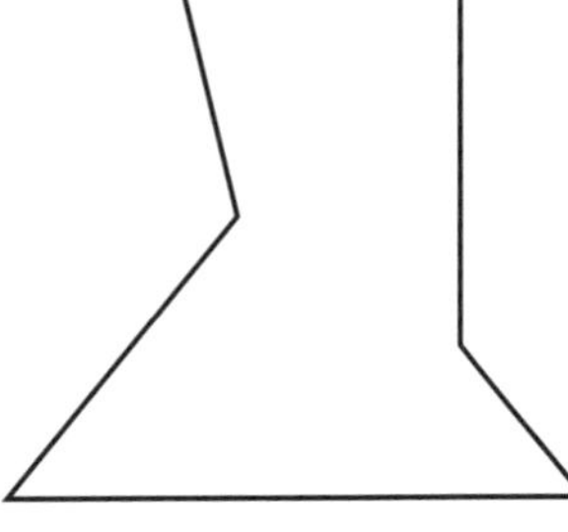
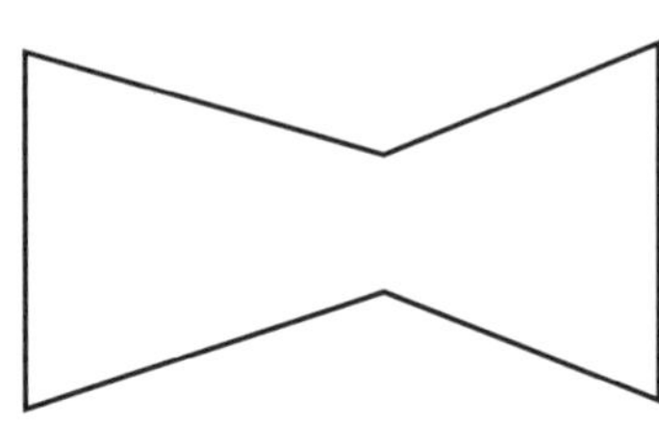

- What are the names of the other shapes?

How easy?

Red
Amber
Green

How do you think you have done?

Name Date

2D and 3D shapes (2)

- Draw lines to show where each 3D shape should go in the Carroll diagram.

6 faces	Not 6 faces

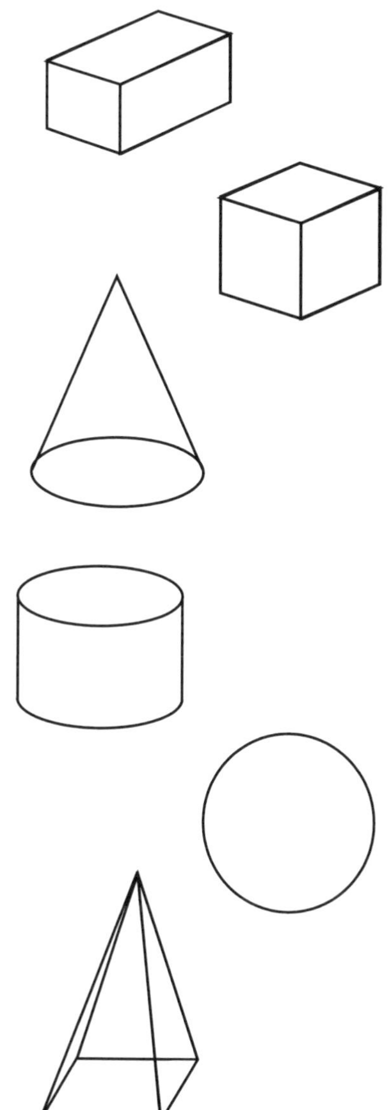

- Name each shape. Here are the words you will need:

cone cylinder cube sphere pyramid cuboid

How easy?

Red
Amber
Green

How do you think you have done?

Name Date

2D and 3D shapes (3)

Number	Shape
	Sphere
	Cube
	Cuboid
	Cylinder
	Pyramid
	Cone

How easy?

How do you think you have done?

____

____

BLOCK C

Handling data and measures

Expected prior learning

Check that children can already:

- answer a question by collecting and recording information in a list or table
- present outcomes using practical resources, pictures, block graphs or pictograms
- use diagrams to sort objects into groups according to a given criterion; suggest a different criterion for grouping the same objects
- estimate, measure, weigh and compare objects using suitable uniform non-standard units and measuring instruments, for example a lever balance, metre stick or measuring jug
- name common 2D shapes and 3D solids and describe their features.

Objectives overview

The text in this diagram identifies the focus of mathematics learning within the block.

Key aspects of learning

- Enquiry
- Information processing
- Social skills
- Reasoning

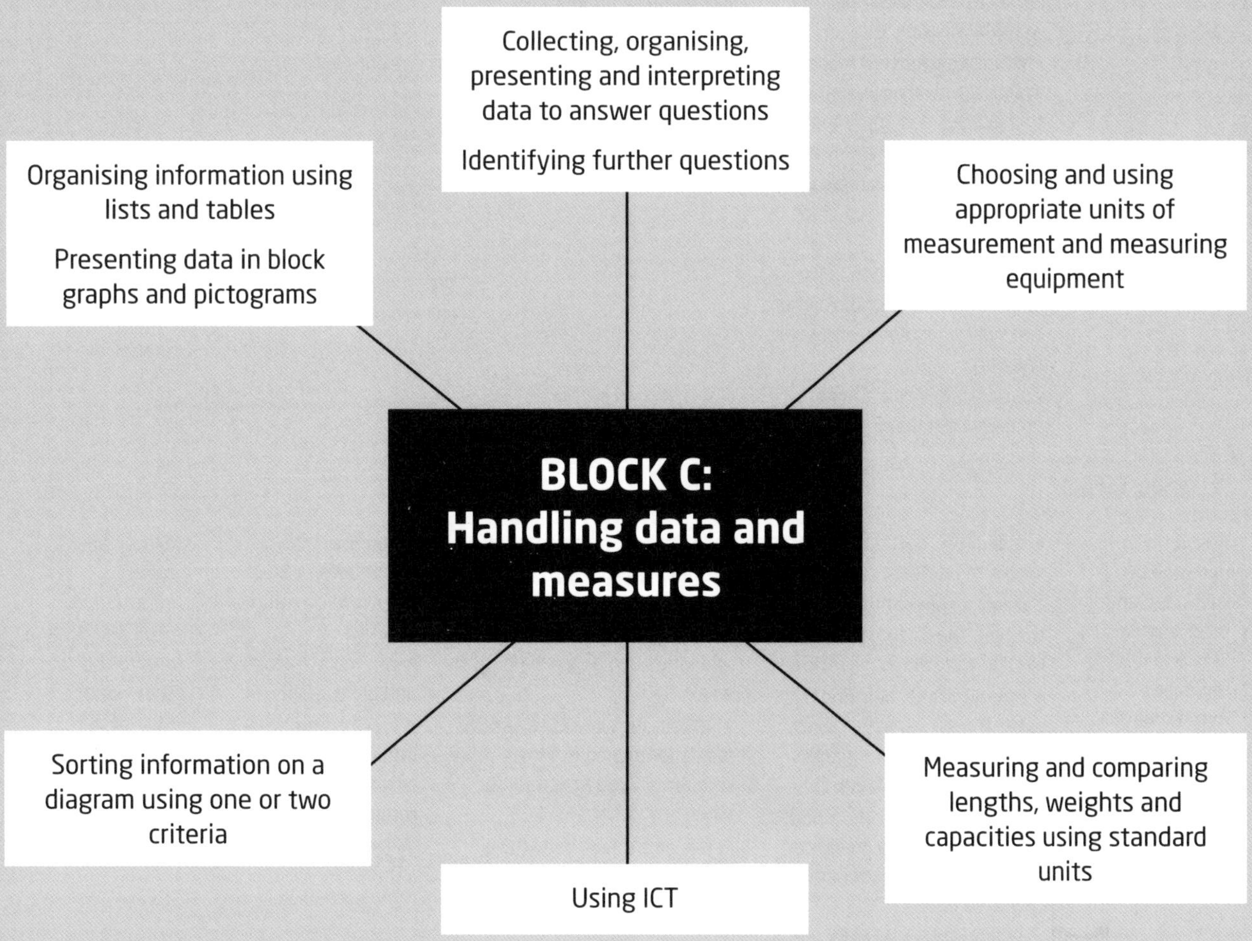

BLOCK C

BLOCK C: Handling data and measures

Collecting, organising, presenting and interpreting data to answer questions

Identifying further questions

Organising information using lists and tables

Presenting data in block graphs and pictograms

Choosing and using appropriate units of measurement and measuring equipment

Sorting information on a diagram using one or two criteria

Using ICT

Measuring and comparing lengths, weights and capacities using standard units

Unit 1 Handling data and measures

Introduction

In this unit, children answer questions and follow lines of enquiry by processing, presenting and interpreting data within various contexts such as measurement, shape and number. They use their findings to make comparisons and draw conclusions. They collect data and classify objects and numbers, organising them in lists and simple tables. They begin to use Carroll diagrams as a means of sorting to one criterion and use the associated vocabulary. They use standard units of measure to sort and compare lengths, weights and capacities. The 'using and applying' aspect of the mathematics is threaded throughout the unit.

Framework objectives	Assessment focuses		Success criteria for Year 2	Learning outcomes
	Level 2	Level 1		
(1) Lists				
Follow a line of enquiry; answer questions by choosing and using suitable equipment and selecting, organising and presenting information in lists, tables and simple diagrams	• select the mathematics they use in some classroom activities, e.g. with support • find a starting point, identifying key facts/relevant information • use apparatus, diagrams, role-play, etc to represent and clarify a problem • move between different representations of a problem, e.g. a situation described in words, a diagram, etc • adopt a suggested model or systematic approach, make connections and apply their knowledge to similar situations • record results in simple lists, tables, pictograms and block graphs, e.g. • present information in lists, tables and simple graphs where one symbol or block represents one unit • enter data into a simple computer database	• use mathematics as an integral part of classroom activities, e.g. with support • engage with practical mathematical activities involving sorting, counting and measuring by direct comparison • represent their work, e.g. • use the objects they have sorted as a record • use objects/pictures to create simple block graphs	• can pose questions and answer other people's questions • can choose how to solve problems and organise the information • can communicate findings to each other in pairs, groups and whole class situations	*I can decide what information I need to answer a question.* *I can put information in lists or tables.*
(2) Voting for pets				
Answer a question by collecting and recording data in lists and tables; represent the data as block graphs or pictograms to show results; use ICT to organise and present data	• collect and sort data to test a simple hypothesis, e.g. • count a show of hands to test the hypothesis 'most children in our class are in bed by 7.30pm' • communicate their findings, using the simple lists, tables, pictograms and block graphs they have recorded, e.g. • respond to questions about the data they have presented, e.g. 'How many of our names have five letters?' • pose similar questions about their data for others to answer	• demonstrate the criterion they have used, e.g. • respond to questions about how they have sorted objects and why each object belongs in a set • talk about which set has 'the most', for example, 'Most children stayed at school for lunch' • talk about how they have represented their work	• can use tables, pictograms or block graphs to communicate findings • can make pictograms and block graphs • can interpret the information to answer or make up questions, compare results and make conclusions	*I know how to collect information.* *I can use lists and tables to show what I found out.*

BLOCK C

Framework objectives	Assessment focuses Level 2	Level 1	Success criteria for Year 2	Learning outcomes
3 Sports				
Use lists, tables and diagrams to sort objects; explain choices using appropriate language, including 'not'	• collect and sort data to test a simple hypothesis, e.g. • count a show of hands to test the hypothesis 'most children in our class are in bed by 7.30pm' • record results in simple lists, tables, pictograms and block graphs, e.g • present information in lists, tables and simple graphs where one symbol or block represents one unit • enter data into a simple computer database • understand vocabulary relating to handling data, e.g. • understand vocabulary such as sort, group, set, list, table, most common, most popular	• sort and classify objects, e.g. • sort using one criterion or sort into disjoint sets using two simple criteria such as boy/girl or thick/thin • sort objects again using a different criterion • sort objects into a given large-scale Venn or Carroll diagram • represent their work, e.g. • use the objects they have sorted as a record • use objects/pictures to create simple block graphs	• can use diagrams to sort objects • can suggest and use a different criterion for sorting the same objects • can compare sets of results and use their comparisons to answer questions	*I can sort objects and talk about how I sorted them.*
4 More or less?				
Estimate, compare and measure lengths, weights and capacities, choosing and using standard units (m, cm, kg, litre) and suitable measuring instruments	• begin to use everyday non-standard and standard units to measure length and mass • begin to understand that numbers can be used not only to count discrete objects but also to describe continuous measures, e.g. length • know which measuring tools to use to find, for example, how much an object weighs, how tall a child is, how long it takes to run around the edge of the playground, how much water it takes to fill the water tray • read scales to the nearest labelled division • begin to make sensible estimates In relation to familiar units	• measure and order objects using direct comparison • compare lengths directly and put them in order • respond to and use the language of comparison: longer, longest, shorter, shortest, more, less, heavier, lighter • check which of two objects is heavier/lighter and begin to put three objects into order • find objects that are longer/shorter than a metre, heavier/lighter than 500 grams, hold more/less than 1 litre	• can use standard units to make realistic estimates • can answer questions such as: 'Is the door taller or shorter than a metre?' • can use standard units to measure and compare objects	*I can find out if something is longer or shorter than a metre.*

BLOCK C

Unit 1 Handling data and measures

Framework objectives	Assessment focuses		Success criteria for Year 2	Learning outcomes
	Level 2	Level 1		
(5) How long?				
Read the numbered divisions on a scale, and interpret the divisions between them (e.g. on a scale from 0 to 25 with intervals of 1 shown but only the divisions 0, 5, 10, 15 and 20 numbered); use a ruler to draw and measure lines to the nearest centimetre	• begin to use everyday non-standard and standard units to measure length and mass • begin to understand that numbers can be used not only to count discrete objects but also to describe continuous measures, e.g. length • know which measuring tools to use to find, for example, how much an object weighs, how tall a child is, how long it takes to run around the edge of the playground, how much water it takes to fill the water tray • read scales to the nearest labelled division • begin to make sensible estimates in relation to familiar units	• measure and order objects using direct comparison • compare lengths directly and put them in order • respond to and use the language of comparison: longer, longest, shorter, shortest, more, less, heavier, lighter • check which of two objects is heavier/lighter and begin to put three objects into order • find objects that are longer/shorter than a metre, heavier/lighter than 500 grams, hold more/less than 1 litre	• can use standard units for measurement • can suggest suitable standard units to estimate and measure	*I can read numbers on a scale.*

BLOCK C

Activity 1

Prior learning
Children can pose and answer questions. They can choose how to solve problems and organise information. They can communicate their findings to each other.

Framework objective
Follow a line of enquiry; answer questions by choosing and using suitable equipment and selecting, organising and presenting information in lists, tables and simple diagrams

Vocabulary
problem, question, explain, predict, pattern, collect, organise, compare, order, sort, group, classify, same, different, property, represent, interpret, count, tally, vote

Resources
Resource sheet: Self-assessment

1 Lists

Say: *A friend of mine wants to organise a party and wants to know what food to provide.* Ask the children to talk to a partner about what she could do. Establish that she could make a list of party food and decide from that. With the class, make a list of party foods on the board. Say that your friend only wants to provide five different sorts of food. Ask them what they should do: vote. Target specific children to answer. Take a vote and ask the children to make a list of the foods she should provide. Decide whether to use the self-assessment sheet for children to record their achievements and what they need to do next.

Teacher support
Less confident learners: Work with these children as your focus group. Provide apparatus to represent different food items. Ask individuals questions and assess their responses.
More confident learners: Ask these children to make a table to show all the results from the vote.

Common misconceptions
Children do not understand the concept of making a list.
Ask the children to tell you the names of some of their friends. Make a list of these for them so that they can see how a list is written. Ask them to make a list of drinks.

Children do not interpret a vote correctly.
Make a list of four foods and ask the children to vote for their favourite. Discuss the results with the children, asking questions such as: *Which is the largest number of votes? What does that mean?*

Probing questions
- What information do you need to answer the question?
- Is a vote a good idea? Why?
- Is a list a good way to present information? Why?

Next steps
Support: To reinforce and consolidate, ask the children to make more lists of different things. If they have difficulty writing, encourage them to draw pictures or diagrams, or provide practical apparatus for them to use. See also Year 1 Block C Unit 3.
Extension: Ask the children to make a list of animals and to ask their classmates to vote for their favourite. They then put this information into a table. See also Year 2 Block C Unit 2.

Activity 2

Prior learning
Children can choose how to communicate their findings using tables, pictograms or block graphs where one block represents one. They can interpret the information, compare results and make conclusions.

Framework objective
Answer a question by collecting and recording data in lists and tables; represent the data as block graphs or pictograms to show results; use ICT to organise and present data

Vocabulary
information, graph, block graph, pictogram, diagram, symbol, set, list, table, label, title

Resources
Interactive activity: Voting for pets
Resource sheet: Self-assessment
Classroom resources: counters

2 Voting for pets

Ask the children you specifically wish to assess how they could find out which is the most popular pet in the class. Reveal the interactive activity 'Voting for pets'. Take the votes and ask targeted questions about the results such as: *Which of these pets is the most popular? Can we tell how many children like hamsters best?* (No, because 'hamsters' wasn't one of the choices.) Ask the children to make a list of the pets in order of popularity and then draw a table to compare them. Decide whether to use the self-assessment sheet for children to record their achievements and what they need to do next.

Teacher support
Less confident learners: Guide these children to ensure that they look at the number of votes in order to make their list.
More confident learners: Ask these children to use the information in their table to make up some statements that involve addition or subtraction.

Common misconceptions
Children do not recognise the numbers in a vote.
Ask the children to count out counters for the different numbers of votes. They may benefit from doing this on a number track. They should then compare the numbers, saying which is the most and which is the least.

Children have difficulty making a table.
Draw the frame of a table with headings for the children, clearly explaining what you are doing. Together add the information to it. Encourage them to make one of their own.

Probing questions
- How did we collect the information?
- What does your list show? What else?
- What is different between the list and the table? What is the same?

Next steps
Support: To reinforce and consolidate, give the children a list of votes on a topic and ask them to make a table using this information, then to think of statements to tell you what their table shows. See also Year 1 Block C Unit 3.
Extension: Give the children the opportunity to make up their own topic, count votes, make lists and tables and compare the two, deciding on which they think is the best way to show the information and why. See also Year 2 Block C Unit 2.

BLOCK C

Activity 3

Prior learning
Children can use diagrams to sort objects using one criterion. They can suggest and use a different criterion to re-sort the same objects. They can compare both sets of results.

Framework objective
Use lists, tables and diagrams to sort objects; explain choices using appropriate language, including 'not'

Vocabulary
information, graph, block graph, pictogram, diagram, symbol, set, list, table, label, title

Resources
Resource sheet: Sports
Classroom resources: A3 paper and pens, dominoes

Sports

Discuss different sports activities and make a list of the children's suggestions. (You may need to add some.) There should be a mixture of those that use balls, nets and neither – for example, rounders, baseball, rugby, tennis, swimming, gymnastics. Discuss ways of sorting the sports into two groups, for instance, balls/no balls, team/not team. Give a set of sports cards (cut from the resource sheet 'Sports') and a piece of A3 paper to pairs of children. Ask them to agree how to sort the sports and stick the cards in two groups on the paper. Observe pairs who you particularly wish to assess.

Teacher support
Less confident learners: Write the headings 'ball' and 'no ball' on A3 paper. Show the children a card, and discuss the sport. *Is it played with a ball? Where does it belong?*
More confident learners: Give these children two sets of cards and ask them to sort the sets in two different ways.

Common misconception
Children cannot sort into a diagram.
Give each child ten dominoes and ask them to identify which dominoes have less than five spots in total. Once they have done this, ask them to put them on a piece of paper. Ask them to put the others on another piece of paper and together compare their groups.

Probing questions
- What other sport could you put here?
- Why is this sport not here?
- How many of the sports need a ball?

Next steps
Support: Give more opportunities to sort in this way during cross-curricular activities – for example, during science the children can sort items that use electricity and those that don't. See also Year 1 Block C Unit 3.
Extension: Ask the children to sort the sports using loops that intersect (a Venn diagram). For example, one loop for 'net', one for 'ball'. They sort the cards into the appropriate spaces, placing those that use both net and ball into the overlapping area. See also Year 2 Block C Unit 2.

Activity 4

Prior learning
Children can use make realistic estimates. They can use standard units to measure and compare objects.

Framework objective
Estimate, compare and measure lengths, weights and capacities, choosing and using standard units (m, cm, kg, litre) and suitable measuring instruments

Vocabulary
about the same as, enough, not enough, too much, too little, too many, too few, nearly, roughly, about, close to, just over, just under, unit, metre (m), metre stick, tape measure, length, width, size, long, longer, longest, short, tall, high, low, wide

Resources
Resource sheet: Self-assessment
Classroom resources: metre sticks, A3 paper and pens, litre containers, 30cm rulers and 10cm paper strips

4 More or less?

Provide small groups of children with a metre stick. Their task is to find and then measure five things that they estimate are longer than 1 metre, five things shorter than 1 metre and one thing that is approximately 1 metre. They should then sort their information and draw the items on A3 paper in a three-sectioned diagram with headings '< 1m', 'about 1m' and '> 1m'. Work with groups of children to observe how they measure and how they record in the diagram. Decide whether to use the self-assessment sheet for children to record their achievements and what they need to do next.

Teacher support
Less confident learners: Compare four items with a metre stick and sort them into two groups: 'shorter than 1 metre' and 'longer than 1 metre'.
More confident learners: Once they have made their diagram, ask children to repeat this investigation to sort containers that hold more or less than 1 litre.

Common misconceptions
Children do not use a metre stick correctly when measuring.
Chalk a starting mark on the floor and ask the children to place one end of the stick onto it. Place some books side by side from the chalk mark and ask them to tell you whether they total a metre or not by comparing both lengths.

Children cannot estimate whether objects are longer or shorter than 1 metre.
Create opportunities outside the lesson to ask the children to tell you if they think something is longer or shorter than 1 metre.

Probing questions
- Can you show me something that is longer/shorter than a metre?
- Do you think you are shorter/taller than a metre?
- How can you check whether you are right?

Next steps
Support: Give the children different items to measure against a metre stick and say whether they are more or less than a metre. Encourage them to estimate first and then check. Have them record their findings using drawings in a given Carroll diagram. See also Year 1 Block C Unit 3.
Extension: Give the children opportunities to measure different items against a 30cm ruler and then 10cm paper strips. They first estimate the length and then measure and record their findings in a Carroll diagram. See also Year 2 Block C Unit 2.

Activity 5

Prior learning

Children are increasingly accurate in their measurements. They suggest suitable standard or uniform non-standard units to estimate and measure.

Framework objective

Read the numbered divisions on a scale, and interpret the divisions between them (e.g. on a scale from 0 to 25 with intervals of 1 shown but only the divisions 0, 5, 10, 15 and 20 numbered); use a ruler to draw and measure lines to the nearest centimetre

Vocabulary

unit, centimetre (cm), metre (m), kilogram (kg), half-kilogram, litre (l), half-litre, ruler, metre stick, tape measure, balance, scales, container, measuring jug, capacity, weight, length

Resources

Resource sheets: Self-assessment, 0-30 number lines, 0-100 number lines
Classroom resources: 30cm rulers, metre sticks, measuring jugs, water, A3 paper and pens

5 How long?

Give each child a sheet of A3 paper and ask them to draw lines of given lengths to the nearest centimetre (for example, 10cm, 15cm, 30cm, 19cm). Once they have drawn these, they should swap their paper with a partner and use a ruler to check that their partner's lines are correct. Observe how the children both draw and check, particularly noting if they start at the correct point on the ruler. Work with small groups to check whether they can read a scale on a measuring jug by asking them to fill it to just under/over half a litre, then 1 litre. Decide whether to use the self-assessment sheet for children to record their achievements and what they need to do next.

Teacher support

Less confident learners: Ask the children to measure and check lines to the nearest 10cm, and compare amounts to 1 litre.
More confident learners: Ask these children to measure lines to the nearest half centimetre.

Common misconceptions

Children do not begin measuring at the zero mark.
Highlight the zero mark with a pen or sticky tape to remind the children where to begin measuring.

Children do not relate a ruler to a number line.
Show a 0–30 number line and compare this with a ruler, asking children what is the same and what is different. Cover up various centimetre notations on the ruler and ask them to use the number line to identify those you have covered.

Probing questions

- What length does this mark show on the ruler?
- What length could be between 5 and 10 on the ruler?
- What length does this mark show on the metre stick? How do you know?

Next steps

Support: To reinforce and consolidate, link scales with a number line. Show a 0–100 number line, a metre stick and a measuring cylinder. Ask children to find certain numbers on each measuring device. See also Year 1 Block C Unit 3.
Extension: Provide opportunities for the children to measure the length of objects in centimetres and to measure the capacity of containers in millilitres. See also Year 2 Block C Unit 2.

Unit 2 Handling data and measures

Introduction

The first part of this unit focuses on collecting, organising, presenting and analysing data in tables, lists, pictograms and block charts. The children are encouraged to evaluate the different methods of data handling with regard to their suitability in each case. The rest of the unit concentrates on the three measures of length, mass and capacity, where the children are expected to estimate, compare and measure using standard units. Reading scales and interpreting the divisions are regularly revisited throughout this part of the unit through demonstrating, modelling and practical measuring. The 'using and applying' aspect of mathematics is threaded throughout the unit.

Framework objectives	Assessment focuses		Success criteria for Year 2	Learning outcomes
	Level 2	Level 1		
1 Land, sea or both				
Follow a line of enquiry; answer questions by choosing and using suitable equipment and selecting, organising and presenting information in lists, tables and simple diagrams	• select the mathematics they use in some classroom activities, e.g. with support • find a starting point, identifying key facts/relevant information • use apparatus, diagrams, role-play, etc to represent and clarify a problem • move between different representations of a problem, e.g. a situation described in words, a diagram, etc • adopt a suggested model or systematic approach, make connections and apply their knowledge to similar situations • record results in simple lists, tables, pictograms and block graphs, e.g. • present information in lists, tables and simple graphs where one symbol or block represents one unit • enter data into a simple computer database	• use mathematics as an integral part of classroom activities, e.g. with support • engage with practical mathematical activities involving sorting, counting and measuring by direct comparison • represent their work, e.g. • use the objects they have sorted as a record • use objects/pictures to create simple block graphs	• can process, present and interpret data to answer a question and follow lines of enquiry • can use various contexts, including measures and those in cross-curricular subjects, to generate data which enable making comparisons and drawing conclusions	*I can organise information and make lists and tables.*

BLOCK C

Unit 2 Handling data and measures

Framework objectives	Assessment focuses		Success criteria for Year 2	Learning outcomes
	Level 2	Level 1		
(2) Favourite food				
Answer a question by collecting and recording data in lists and tables; represent the data as block graphs or pictograms to show results; use ICT to organise and present data	• collect and sort data to test a simple hypothesis, e.g. • count a show of hands to test the hypothesis 'Most children in our class are in bed by 7.30pm' • communicate their findings, using the simple lists, tables, pictograms and block graphs they have recorded, e.g. • respond to questions about the data they have presented, e.g. 'How many of our names have 5 letters?' • pose similar questions about their data for others to answer	• demonstrate the criterion they have used, e.g. • respond to questions about how they have sorted objects and why each object belongs in a set • talk about which set has most, for example, 'Most children stayed at school for lunch' • talk about how they have represented their work	• can justify choices of where to place shapes, numbers or objects into lists and tables • can choose different criteria for sorting the same set of objects and explain this to others	*I can make block graphs and get information from other people's graphs.*
(3) Multiples				
Use lists, tables and diagrams to sort objects; explain choices using appropriate language, including 'not'	• collect and sort data to test a simple hypothesis, e.g. • count a show of hands to test the hypothesis 'Most children in our class are in bed by 7.30pm' • record results in simple lists, tables, pictograms and block graphs, e.g. • present information in lists, tables and simple graphs where one symbol or block represents one unit • enter data into a simple computer database • understand vocabulary relating to handling data, e.g. • understand vocabulary such as sort, group, set, list, table, most common, most popular	• sort and classify objects, e.g. • sort using one criterion or sort into disjoint sets using two simple criteria such as boy/girl or thick/thin • sort objects again using a different criterion • sort objects into a given large-scale Venn or Carroll diagram • represent their work, e.g. • use the objects they have sorted as a record • use objects/pictures to create simple block graphs	• can use lists, tables and diagrams to sort objects using one criterion • can choose different criteria for re-sorting the objects into another diagram • can discuss the meaning of 'not' and use this as one of the criterion on a diagram • can solve problems and respond to questions related to their lists, tables and diagrams	*I can sort objects and use diagrams to show how I sorted them.*

BLOCK C

Unit 2 Handling data and measures

Framework objectives	Assessment focuses		Success criteria for Year 2	Learning outcomes
	Level 2	Level 1		
4 Heavier or lighter?				
Estimate, compare and measure lengths, weights and capacities, choosing and using standard units (m, cm, kg, litre) and suitable measuring instruments	• begin to use everyday non-standard and standard units to measure length and mass • begin to understand that numbers can be used not only to count discrete objects but also to describe continuous measures e.g. length • know which measuring tools to use to find, for example, how much an object weighs, how tall a child is, how long it takes to run around the edge of the playground, how much water it takes to fill the water tray • read scales to the nearest labelled division • begin to make sensible estimates in relation to familiar units	• measure and order objects using direct comparison • compare lengths directly and put them in order • respond to and use the language of comparison: longer, longest, shorter, shortest, more, less, heavier, lighter • check which of two objects is heavier/lighter and begin to put three objects into order • find objects that are longer/ shorter than a metre, heavier/ lighter than 500 grams, hold more/less than 1 litre	• can use standard units of measure to make realistic estimates and answer questions • can follow a line of enquiry by, for example, sorting a set of containers according to whether they will hold a litre of water or more or less than a litre • can then place this information into a diagram	*I can estimate whether an object is heavier or lighter than a half-kilogram by putting a half-kilogram weight in one hand and the object in the other.*
5 Measuring length				
Read the numbered divisions on a scale, and interpret the divisions between them (e.g. on a scale from 0 to 25 with intervals of 1 shown but only the divisions 0, 5, 10, 15 and 20 numbered); use a ruler to draw and measure lines to the nearest centimetre	• begin to use everyday non-standard and standard units to measure length and mass • begin to understand that numbers can be used not only to count discrete objects but also to describe continuous measures e.g. length • know which measuring tools to use to find, for example, how much an object weighs, how tall a child is, how long it takes to run around the edge of the playground, how much water it takes to fill the water tray • read scales to the nearest labelled division • begin to make sensible estimates in relation to familiar units	• measure and order objects using direct comparison • compare lengths directly and put them in order • respond to and use the language of comparison: longer, longest, shorter, shortest, more, less, heavier, lighter • check which of two objects is heavier/lighter and begin to put three objects into order • find objects that are longer/ shorter than a metre, heavier/ lighter than 500 grams, hold more/less than 1 litre	• can compare lengths against a metre rule or 30cm ruler, weights of various objects against kilogram and half-kilogram weights and capacities against a litre and half-litre • can read the vertical axis going up in ones on a block graph	*I can use a ruler or metre stick to measure how long something is.* *I can read numbers on a scale and work out the numbers between them.*

Activity 1

Prior learning
Children can process, present and interpret data. They generate data that can be used for making comparisons and drawing conclusions.

Framework objective
Follow a line of enquiry; answer questions by choosing and using suitable equipment and selecting, organising and presenting information in lists, tables and simple diagrams

Vocabulary
problem, question, explain, predict, pattern, collect, organise, compare, order, sort, group, classify, same, different, property, represent, interpret, count, tally, vote

Resources
Resource sheets: Land, sea or both, Self-assessment
Classroom resources: dice, scissors, glue, A3 paper and pens

1 Land, sea or both

Give the resource sheet 'Land, sea or both' to pairs of children. Explain that they need to look at the pictures and think about where the animals live. Ask them to cut out the pictures and use them to make three lists of animals - one for animals that live only in the sea, one for those that live on land and one for those that live in both - by sticking the pictures in appropriate places on a sheet of A3 paper and labelling their lists. Once they have done this, ask them to make a table to show the information. Decide whether to use the self-assessment sheet for children to record their achievements and what they need to do next.

Teacher support
Less confident learners: Prepare this activity for the children by drawing and labelling rectangles for their lists, cutting out the pictures, and drawing and labelling the frame for their table.
More confident learners: Challenge these children to think of two more animals to fit in each group, then add them and make a new table.

Common misconceptions
Children do not understand the concept of making a list.
Ask the children to tell you the names of some of their friends. Make a list of these for them so that they can see how one is written. Repeat this for their favourite animals. Ask them to make one for drinks.

Children do not understand the concept of a table.
Make a simple table to show how many boys and girls are in the class and describe it to the children. Then ask questions such as: *What does this part tell us? How many girls are there?*

Probing questions
- What headings do you need for the table?
- Why is the table a useful way to show the information?
- What does the list tell us that the table doesn't?

Next steps
Support: Ask the children to make simple tables (for example, for dice scores). They should draw their table with the numbers 1 to 6 in one column. They throw a dice six times, each time making a tick beside each number they score. See also Year 2 Block A Unit 1.
Extension: Encourage the children to make their own tables and choose the information they want to record in them (for example, colours of clothes other children are wearing). See also Year 2 Block C Unit 3.

Activity 2

Prior learning
Children can justify their placement of shapes, numbers or objects in lists and tables they have made. They can choose different criteria to re-sort the objects.

Framework objective
Answer a question by collecting and recording data in lists and tables; represent the data as block graphs or pictograms to show results; use ICT to organise and present data

Vocabulary
information, graph, block graph, pictogram, diagram, symbol, set, list, table, label, title

Resources
Interactive activity: Favourite food
Resource sheet: Self-assessment
Classroom resources: A4 paper, interlocking cubes (in different colours)

2 Favourite food

Discuss the children's favourite foods, making a list on the board. Ask them to vote for their favourites. Next, reveal the interactive activity 'Favourite food', and ask the children to each vote for which food they like best. Add the number of votes to the data table. Ask questions that involve reading the data and also finding totals and differences, such as: *How many more children like ice cream than chips best? How many children like fruit best? How many like chocolate cake best?* Click 'create bar chart' and show the graph. The children should then use this information to make a pictogram. Decide whether to use the self-assessment sheet for children to record their achievements and next steps.

Teacher support
Less confident learners: Give the children a frame for their pictogram, labelled if you think this would be helpful.
More confident learners: Ask the children to make a block graph to show favourite hobbies. Let them collect their information by asking the rest of class.

Common misconceptions
Children have difficulty interpreting data from a block graph.
Work on this practically, using linking cubes. Set up a scenario that involves favourite flavours of ice cream (for example, tower of two pink cubes for strawberry, three brown for chocolate etc). Stand them up side by side and ask questions such as: *Which flavour is most popular? How do you know?*

Children have difficulty understanding the vertical axis.
Link the graph to a number line, placing it vertically and comparing the two.

Probing questions
- Why is a block graph a good way to show this information?
- What is the same about a block graph and a pictogram?
- What is different?

Next steps
Support: Use cubes to demonstrate how a block graph is made. Ask the children to collect different sets of data and then record their findings in cube towers of different colours. Stand these up against a sheet of paper and ask the children to label the block graph. See also Year 2 Block A Unit 1.
Extension: Give the children opportunities to collect different data that they then represent on block graphs and pictograms that they draw unaided. See also Year 2 Block C Unit 3.

Activity 3

Prior learning
Children can use lists, tables and diagrams to sort objects using one criterion. They can discuss the meaning of 'not'. They can solve problems related to their lists, tables and diagrams.

Framework objective
Use lists, tables and diagrams to sort objects; explain choices using appropriate language, including 'not'

Vocabulary
information, graph, block graph, pictogram, diagram, symbol, set, list, table, label, title

Resources
Resource sheets: Self-assessment, 0–20 number cards, Venn diagram
Classroom resources: coloured cubes

3 Multiples

Discuss the word 'multiple' and count in steps of 2 and 5 from zero to the tenth multiple. Draw a diagram with two columns, one headed 'multiple of 2' and the other 'not multiple of 2'. Ask the children to give you different numbers to go under each heading. Ask them to draw a similar diagram for 'multiple of 5'/'not multiple of 5' and to add at least ten numbers to each section. Observe the children as they work. Decide whether to use the self-assessment sheet for children to record their achievements and what they need to do next.

Teacher support
Less confident learners: Draw and label the diagram. Give the children number cards to 20 and ask them to place each card in the appropriate section.
More confident learners: Ask the children to complete a diagram that has three columns headed 'multiple of 2', 'multiple of 5' and 'multiple of 2 and 5'.

Common misconception
Children cannot sort into a diagram.
Give each child about ten cubes of various colours. Ask them to identify all the blue cubes and put them on a piece of paper. Next, ask them to put the other cubes on another piece of paper and decide what headings could be written for each group ('blue' and 'not blue').

Probing questions
- What have you put this number in this section of the diagram?
- Have you any numbers that are in both parts? Why is that?
- What else could be put here?

Next steps
Support: Provide more opportunities to sort in this way using 'not' in other areas of maths. For example, when sorting shapes into those that have curved faces and those that do not, consider what to do with shapes such as a cone that have both. See also Year 2 Block A Unit 1.
Extension: Ask children to sort items into a simple Venn diagram (for example, one circle for multiples of 2, one for multiples of 5 and the intersection for numbers that are multiples of both 2 and 5). See also Year 2 Block C Unit 3.

Activity 4

Prior learning
Children can use standard units of measure to estimate. They can follow a line of enquiry. They can then place information into a diagram.

Framework objective
Estimate, compare and measure lengths, weights and capacities, choosing and using standard units (m, cm, kg, litre) and suitable measuring instruments

Vocabulary
about the same as, enough, not enough, too much, too little, too many, too few, nearly, roughly, about, close to, just over, just under, unit, metre (m), metre stick, tape measure, length, width, size, long, longer, longest, short, tall, high, low, wide

Resources
Resource sheets: Heavier or lighter?, Self-assessment
Classroom resources: classroom items, foodstuffs (eg potatoes), weighing scales, half-kilogram and one kilogram weights, A3 paper, pens, scissors, glue

4 Heavier or lighter?

Show various classroom items and some foodstuffs. Ask the children to estimate whether these are heavier or lighter than half a kilogram. Invite those you wish to assess to check their answers using scales. Give each child the resource sheet 'Heavier or lighter?'. They cut out each picture and decide whether the item it shows will be heavier or lighter than ½kg and make two piles accordingly. They then order each pile of pictures from lightest to heaviest and make a diagram in order of weight. Decide whether to use the self-assessment sheet for children to record their achievements and what they need to do next.

Teacher support
Less confident learners: Have these children concentrate on comparing real items with a half-kilogram weight and drawing their pictures in a diagram.
More confident learners: Once they have made their diagram, ask the children to add a third column and to draw things in it that would be heavier than 1kg.

Common misconceptions
Children have difficulty reading scales.
Make specific links to number lines, rulers and measuring cylinders. Draw a number line on a strip of paper and then cut snips into it so that you can curve it round to resemble the circular scale on weighing scales.

Children cannot estimate whether objects are heavier or lighter than ½kg.
Give plenty of opportunities to do this practically, by holding a ½kg weight in one hand and an item in their other hand. Begin with items that are obviously more or less than ½kg.

Probing questions
- Can you show me something that is heavier/lighter than ½kg?
- Do you think this is heavier/lighter than 1kg?
- How can you check whether you are right?

Next steps
Support: Give the children different items to measure against an object weighing ½kg and say whether they are more or less than this. Encourage them to estimate first and then check and record their findings using a simple diagram. See also Year 2 Block A Unit 1.
Extension: Give children opportunities to collect up to ten items and order them from lightest to heaviest and then to draw these in a diagram and mark 0kg, 1kg and ½kg. They check their choices, using scales. See also Year 2 Block C Unit 3.

Activity 5

Prior learning

Children can compare lengths against a ruler, weights against a kilogram and half-kilogram and capacities against a litre and half-litre. They can read the vertical axis of a block graph.

Framework objective

Read the numbered divisions on a scale, and interpret the divisions between them (e.g. on a scale from 0 to 25 with intervals of 1 shown but only the divisions 0, 5, 10, 15 and 20 numbered); use a ruler to draw and measure lines to the nearest centimetre

Vocabulary

unit, centimetre (cm), metre (m), kilogram (kg), half-kilogram, litre (l), half-litre, ruler, metre stick, tape measure, balance, scales, container, measuring jug, capacity, weight, length

Resources

Resource sheet: Self-assessment
Classroom resources: 30cm ruler, metre rule, 10cm paper strips, 0–100 number line

Measuring length

Work with small groups of children and observe their ability to measure a variety of objects using metre rules and rulers. Before they begin, ask them to choose five items, two of which they think would be measured with a ruler (for example, an eraser), two with a metre rule (for example, height of a chair) and one that could use both (for example, length of a table). They then measure their chosen objects as accurately as they can and record their measurements in a table. Decide whether to use the self-assessment sheet for children to record their achievements and what they need to do next.

Teacher support

Less confident learners: Ask these children to think of things to be measured with a ruler and help them measure to the nearest centimetre.
More confident learners: Have these children measure items that need a metre rule because they are between 30cm and 100cm long/high (so that they have a more challenging scale to interpret).

Common misconceptions

Children do not begin measuring at the first mark on a ruler or metre rule.
Highlight the first mark with a pen or sticky tape to remind the children.

Children do not relate a metre rule to a number line.
Show a 0–100 number line and compare this with a metre rule. Ask children what is the same and what is different. Cover up various marks on the ruler and ask children to use the number line to identify them.

Probing questions

- What can you think of that needs to be measured with a metre rule?
- Do these things have to be over 1 metre? Why not?
- How would you measure something that was just over 1 metre?

Next steps

Support: Give the children 10cm strips of paper and ask them to measure using these and to count in tens to give the length in centimetres (for example, four strips of paper is 40cm). Encourage the children to use the terms 'just under', 'just over' and 'nearly'. See also Year 2 Block A Unit 1.
Extension: Encourage the children to practise reading metre rules more accurately, – for example, the mark between 50 and 60 centimetres would be approximately 55cm. See also Year 2 Block C Unit 3.

Unit 3 Handling data and measures

Introduction

In this unit, children answer questions and follow lines of enquiry by processing, presenting and interpreting data within various contexts such as measurement, shape and number. They use their findings to make comparisons and draw conclusions. They collect data and classify objects and numbers, organising them in lists and simple tables. They begin to use Carroll diagrams as a means of sorting to one criterion and use the associated vocabulary. They use standard units of measure to sort and compare lengths, weights and capacities. The 'using and applying' aspect of the mathematics is threaded throughout the unit.

Framework objectives	Assessment focuses		Success criteria for Year 2	Learning outcomes
	Level 2	Level 1		
(1) Cereal				
Follow a line of enquiry; answer questions by choosing and using suitable equipment and selecting, organising and presenting information in lists, tables and simple diagrams	• select the mathematics they use in some classroom activities, e.g. with support • find a starting point, identifying key facts/relevant information • use apparatus, diagrams, role-play etc to represent and clarify a problem • collect and sort data to test a simple hypothesis, e.g. • count a show of hands to test the hypothesis 'Most children in our class are in bed by 7.30pm' • record results in simple lists, tables, pictograms and block graphs, e.g. • present information in lists, tables and simple graphs where one symbol or block represents one unit • enter data into a simple computer database	• use mathematics as an integral part of classroom activities, e.g. with support • engage with practical mathematical activities involving sorting, counting and measuring by direct comparison • represent their work, e.g. • use the objects they have sorted as a record • use objects/pictures to create simple block graphs	• can work in a group to plan and carry out an enquiry • can consider different ways of approaching a given task, agreeing how they are going to work and who will do what • can present their findings in a list or table and ask and answer questions from it	*I can test out an idea by collecting and organising information.*
(2) Bedtime votes!				
Answer a question by collecting and recording data in lists and tables; represent the data as block graphs or pictograms to show results; use ICT to organise and present data	• collect and sort data to test a simple hypothesis, e.g. • count a show of hands to test the hypothesis 'Most children in our class are in bed by 7.30pm' • communicate their findings, using the simple lists, tables, pictograms and block graphs they have recorded, e.g. • respond to questions about the data they have presented, e.g. 'How many of our names have five letters?' • pose similar questions about their data for others to answer	• demonstrate the criterion they have used, e.g. • respond to questions about how they have sorted objects and why each object belongs in a set • talk about which set has most, for example 'Most children stayed at school for lunch' • talk about how they have represented their work	• can use data handling software to sort shapes and input and read information from block graphs • can explain what they did and their results	*I can use ICT to show results.*

BLOCK C

Unit 3 Handling data and measures

Framework objectives	Assessment focuses: Level 2	Assessment focuses: Level 1	Success criteria for Year 2	Learning outcomes
3 Fruit				
Use lists, tables and diagrams to sort objects; explain choices using appropriate language, including 'not'	• sort objects and classify them using more than one criterion, e.g. • sort a given set of shapes using two criteria such as triangle/not triangle and blue/not blue • collect and sort data to test a simple hypothesis, e.g. • count a show of hands to test the hypothesis 'Most children in our class are in bed by 7.30pm' • record results in simple lists, tables, pictograms and block graphs, e.g. • present information in lists, tables and simple graphs where one symbol or block represents one unit • enter data into a simple computer database • understand vocabulary relating to handling data, e.g. • understand vocabulary such as sort, group, set, list, table, most common, most popular	• sort and classify objects, e.g. • sort using one criterion or sort into disjoint sets using two simple criteria such as boy/girl or thick/thin • sort objects again using a different criterion • sort objects into a given large-scale Venn or Carroll diagram • represent their work, e.g. • use the objects they have sorted as a record • use objects/pictures to create simple block graphs	• can sort objects and use lists, tables and diagrams to show how they have done this according to one criterion of their choice • can sort according to two criteria • can solve problems and respond to questions related to their lists, tables and diagrams	*I can sort objects in different ways and explain how I sorted them.*
4 A litre or not?				
Estimate, compare and measure lengths, weights and capacities, choosing and using standard units (m, cm, kg, litre) and suitable measuring instruments	• begin to use everyday non-standard and standard units to measure length and mass • begin to understand that numbers can be used not only to count discrete objects but also to describe continuous measures e.g. length • know which measuring tools to use to find, for example, how much an object weighs, how tall a child is, how long it takes to run around the edge of the playground, how much water it takes to fill the water tray • read scales to the nearest labelled division • begin to make sensible estimates in relation to familiar units	• measure and order objects using direct comparison • compare lengths directly and put them in order • respond to and use the language of comparison: longer, longest, shorter, shortest, more, less, heavier, lighter • check which of two objects is heavier/lighter and begin to put three objects into order • find objects that are longer/shorter than a metre, heavier/lighter than 500 grams, hold more/less than 1 litre	• can use standard units of measure to make realistic estimates, record measurements and ask and answer questions as they follow a line of inquiry • can place this information onto lists, tables and diagrams	*I can use a measuring jug to measure a litre of water and to find out how much other containers hold.*

BLOCK C

Unit 3 Handling data and measures

Framework objectives	Assessment focuses: Level 2	Assessment focuses: Level 1	Success criteria for Year 2	Learning outcomes
5 Measuring scales				
Read the numbered divisions on a scale, and interpret the divisions between them (e.g. on a scale from 0 to 25 with intervals of 1 shown but only the divisions 0, 5, 10, 15 and 20 numbered); use a ruler to draw and measure lines to the nearest centimetre	• begin to use everyday non-standard and standard units to measure length and mass • begin to understand that numbers can be used not only to count discrete objects but also to describe continuous measures e.g. length • know which measuring tools to use to find, for example, how much an object weighs, how tall a child is, how long it takes to run around the edge of the playground, how much water it takes to fill the water tray • read scales to the nearest labelled division • begin to make sensible estimates in relation to familiar units	• measure and order objects using direct comparison • compare lengths directly and put them in order • respond to and use the language of comparison: longer, longest, shorter, shortest, more, less, heavier, lighter check which of two objects is heavier/lighter and begin to put three objects into order • find objects that are longer/shorter than a metre, heavier/lighter than 500 grams, hold more/less than 1 litre	• can use a metre tape or rule, marked and numbered in centimetres to estimate and measure lengths • can collect this information and display it in lists and also on an ordered table	*I can read scales marked in fives and tens.*

BLOCK C

Activity 1

Prior learning
Children can work together to carry out an enquiry. They are able to present their findings in a list or table.

Framework objective
Follow a line of enquiry; answer questions by choosing and using suitable equipment and selecting, organising and presenting information in lists, tables and simple diagrams

Vocabulary
problem, question, explain, predict, pattern, collect, organise, compare, order, sort, group, classify, same, different, property, represent, interpret, count, tally, vote

Resources
Resource sheet: Self-assessment
Classroom resources: A3 paper and pens

1 Cereal

Present a statement, such as: *More than half our class have cereal for breakfast every day.* Ask the children how they could find out whether this is true. Establish that they could take a show of hands. Together, make a table showing numbers who have cereal every day, sometimes and never. Decide if the statement is true. Now ask them to work in pairs to find out something else that the class has for breakfast. They make a statement, test it out and make a table. Decide whether to use the self-assessment sheet for children to record their achievements and what they need to do next.

Teacher support
Less confident learners: Work with these children, helping them to collect the information and guide them in organising it onto a table.
More confident learners: Ask the children to test out two of their own statements, make lists and tables, then compare them, deciding which the most helpful method is.

Common misconceptions
Children cannot organise information.
Show children how to organise the same information into a list, a table, and different diagrams and discuss what each shows. Encourage them to work with you to make a list and table for breakfast foods that a group of children eat.

Children do not understand the concept of a table.
Make a simple table to show how many children in the class have cereal and how many don't and describe it to them. Then ask questions such as: *What does this part tell us? Where will you look to find out how many don't have cereal?*

Probing questions
- What do you think we will find? Why?
- What information do we need?
- How should we collect it?

Next steps
Support: To reinforce and consolidate, work with the children to represent information such as that gleaned about cereal in a pictogram. See also Year 2 Block A Unit 2.
Extension: Encourage these children to represent tables of information as block graphs and pictograms. See also Year 3 Block C Unit 1.

Activity 2

Prior learning
Children can use simple software to sort shapes and input and read information from block graphs. They can explain their method and results.

Framework objective
Answer a question by collecting and recording data in lists and tables; represent the data as block graphs or pictograms to show results; use ICT to organise and present data

Vocabulary
information, graph, block graph, pictogram, diagram, symbol, set, list, table, label, title

Resources
Interactive activity: Bedtime votes!
Resource sheet: Self-assessment
Classroom resources: wooden blocks or linking cubes (in different colours)

2 Bedtime votes!

Ask the children how they could find out at what time most children in the class go to bed. Reveal the interactive activity 'Bedtime votes!'. Take the vote and input the information. Ask targeted questions about the results such as: *At which time do most children in the class go to bed? How many more children go to bed at 7 o'clock than at 8 o'clock?* Ask the children to create a block graph and then make statements about what they have found out. Let them do this unaided, observing how they tackle the task. Decide whether to use the self-assessment sheet for children to record their achievements and what they need to do next.

Teacher support
Less confident learners: Provide these children with information to put into the interactive activity 'Bedtime votes!'. Once they have made a block graph, ask them questions about what it shows.
More confident learners: Once the children have made their block graph, ask them to draw a pictogram to show the same information.

Common misconception
Children have difficulty interpreting data from a block graph.
Work on this practically, using wooden blocks or linking cubes. Ask children to say their favourite crisp flavour and take a block that represents that colour. They write their name on a sticky note and place it on the side of the block. Make towers of the blocks of the same colour. Stand them up side by side and ask questions such as: *Which flavour is most popular? How do you know?*

Probing questions
- What is the most popular choice?
- What is the least popular choice?
- What is the difference between the most and the least popular?

Next steps
Support: Provide more opportunities for collecting data and representing this as block graphs. The children could use the 'Bedtime votes!' interactive to create their own block graphs, inputting data and then seeing how the block graphs change for different data. See also Year 2 Block A Unit 2.
Extension: Ask the children to use as many ICT programs as are available to create block graphs for the same data. Which do they think is best, and why? See also Year 3 Block C Unit 1.

Activity 3

Prior learning

Children can sort objects according to one criterion and are beginning to sort to two criteria. They can solve problems and answer questions related to their lists, tables and diagrams.

Framework objective

Use lists, tables and diagrams to sort objects; explain choices using appropriate language, including 'not'

Vocabulary

information, graph, block graph, pictogram, diagram, symbol, set, list, table, label, title

Resources

Resource sheet: Self-assessment
Classroom resources: A3 paper and pens, coins

Fruit

Discuss the types of fruit that the children like. Take two of their examples (for example, apples and bananas) and write the names of the children who like them and also those that like neither. From this information ask the children to make a Carroll diagram with horizontal headings 'apples'/'not apples' and vertical headings 'bananas'/'not bananas', filling it with the appropriate children's names. Remind them what a Carroll diagram looks like if necessary. Sit with those you wish to assess, asking them to explain what they are doing and why. Decide whether to use the self-assessment sheet for children to record their achievements and next steps.

Teacher support

Less confident learners: Ask the children to draw a diagram to show who likes/doesn't like one of the fruits. Let them choose which fruit they focus on.
More confident learners: Ask these children to make up at least six statements about the information that their diagram shows.

Common misconceptions

Children cannot sort into a diagram.
Give children a selection of coins and ask them to sort them according to whether they are silver or not. Show them how to draw a simple diagram with labels to put the coins into.

Children cannot identify information from the diagram.
Ask questions that simply require children to read the basic information shown in a diagram, such as: *How many children like bananas?* Ask them to say the answer in a sentence. For example: *Six children like bananas.*

Probing questions

- How many children don't like either fruit?
- How many children like apples? How do you know?
- Where will you look to find who likes both fruits?

Next steps

Support: Repeat the activity for two other fruit. Draw the frame of a two-criteria Carroll diagram and write the headings for the children. Once they have the information, ask them to draw smiley faces to represent the children, rather than writing names. See also Year 2 Block A Unit 2.
Extension: Encourage the children to think of their own investigation. Collect the information and make up a two-criteria Carroll diagram correctly labelled and with the names of the children appropriately placed. See also Year 3 Block C Unit 1.

Activity 4

Prior learning
Children can use standard units of measure to estimate, record measurements and answer questions. They can place information into lists, tables and diagrams.

Framework objective
Estimate, compare and measure lengths, weights and capacities, choosing and using standard units (m, cm, kg, litre) and suitable measuring instruments

Vocabulary
about the same as, enough, not enough, too much, too little, too many, too few, nearly, roughly, about, close to, just over, just under, unit, metre (m), metre stick, tape measure, length, width, size, long, longer, longest, short, tall, high, low, wide

Resources
Resource sheet: Self-assessment
Classroom resources: selection of different containers (for example, ½ litre, l litre and 2 litre bottles, jugs, plastic tubs)

4 A litre or not?

Ask a child you wish to assess to fill a measuring jug to 1 litre and show the class. Next, show one of the other containers and ask the children to put their thumbs up if they think it will hold 1 litre, down if they don't. The child tests this out. Draw a table with three columns: 'holds less than 1 litre', 'holds 1 litre', 'holds more than 1 litre'. Draw the tested container in the appropriate column. In groups, the children then do this for other containers and complete their own table. Decide whether to use the self-assessment sheet for children to record their achievements and what they need to do next.

Teacher support
Less confident learners: Ask these children to complete a table headed 'holds more than 1 litre' and 'holds less than 1 litre'.
More confident learners: Ask these children to complete a table with four columns headed 'holds <1 litre', 'holds 1 litre', 'holds between 1 and 2 litres', 'holds >2 litres'.

Common misconceptions
Children have difficulty reading scales.
Make specific links to number lines, rulers and weighing scales. Draw a number line on a strip of paper and then move it to a vertical position so it is similar to the scale on a measuring jug.

Children cannot estimate whether containers hold more or less than 1 litre.
Give plenty of opportunities to do this practically, always measuring and looking at 1 litre first.

Probing questions
- What units should we measure in?
- Do you think there are 2 litres of water here? How can we find out?
- Which containers do you think might hold one litre?

Next steps
Support: Provide bottles that can be filled with ½ litre, 1 litre or 2 litres of water. Ask the children to fill each and then empty them into a measuring jug to check. Encourage them to explain how they can use the scale on the jug to help them. See also Year 2 Block A Unit 2.
Extension: Ask the children to measure the capacity of different containers to the nearest 100ml, using a measuring jug and recording their measurements on a 0–1000 number line marked in hundreds. See also Year 3 Block C Unit 1.

Activity 5

Prior learning

Children can use a metre rule to estimate lengths. They can use scales to measure weights and measure cylinders for capacity. They can display this information in lists and tables.

Framework objective

Read the numbered divisions on a scale, and interpret the divisions between them (e.g. on a scale from 0 to 25 with intervals of 1 shown but only the divisions 0, 5, 10, 15 and 20 numbered); use a ruler to draw and measure lines to the nearest centimetre

Vocabulary

unit, centimetre (cm), metre (m), kilogram (kg), half-kilogram, litre (l), half-litre, ruler, metre stick, tape measure, balance, scales, container, measuring jug, capacity, weight, length

Resources

Resource sheet: Self-assessment
Classroom resources: paper, pencils, 30cm rulers

5 Measuring scales

Ask the children to make their own measuring scale numbered in fives. To do this they draw a 30cm line, mark off every 5cm and label these marks with the correct numbers, ie 5cm, 10cm, 15cm, 20cm, 25cm and 30cm. Next, ask the children to measure the length of small items using their own measuring scale and to record the lengths in a list to the nearest 5cm. Sit with groups to assess their ability to construct and measure with their scale accurately. Decide whether to use the self-assessment sheet for children to record their achievements and what they need to do next.

Teacher support

Less confident learners: Ask these children to mark their scale in 10cm sections and measure to the nearest 10cm.
More confident learners: Once the children have done this activity, ask them to make a measuring scale that goes up in 2cm sections to make more accurate readings.

Common misconception

When drawing lines of a given length, children begin drawing at the start of the ruler.
Highlight the zero mark on the ruler with a pen or sticky tape to remind the child where to begin measuring.

Probing questions

- What does this mark represent?
- What can help you find out?
- How can knowing our 2-, 5- and 10-times tables help us read these scales?

Next steps

Support: Once they are confident measuring to the nearest 10cm, ask the children to adapt their scale to measure every 5cm and to measure items using this. See also Year 2 Block A Unit 2.
Extension: Encourage these children to make a metre measure, by cutting strips of A3 paper and sticking them together, then marking every 5cm and adding the appropriate numbers. Next, ask them to measure items that are a maximum of 100cm to the nearest 5cm and make a list of their measurements. See also Year 3 Block C Unit 1.

Units 1, 2 & 3 Periodic assessment

These activities can be used at the end of this block to assess those children that you think have achieved the objectives.

Sorting diagrams

Framework objective
Use lists, tables and diagrams to sort objects; explain choices using appropriate language, including 'not' one

Learning outcomes

- I can sort objects and talk about how I sorted them.
- I can sort objects and use diagrams to show how I sorted them.
- I can sort objects in different ways and explain how I sorted them.

1. Provide each child with a copy of the worksheet 'Sorting diagrams (1)'. Ask them to tick all the children who are wearing bobble hats in the illustration, then write down the number. Next, ask them to complete the table on the worksheet. Finally, ask the children to think of a different way to sort the children in the picture. Sit with the group of children whom you particularly wish to assess.

2. Give each child the worksheet 'Sorting diagrams (2)' and ask them to sort the numbers into the correct places on the diagram. Sit with the group of children you particularly wish to assess. Establish that they should sort four ways: numbers that are two-digit and not two-digit and those that are odd and not odd. Recap odd and even numbers. Observe how the children do this and ask questions such as: *Why does 7 go here? Where should I put 83?*

3. Give the children a copy of the worksheet 'Sorting diagrams (3)'. Ask them to cut out the pictures from the resource sheet 'Sorting diagrams (4)' and think of criteria with which to sort the pictures. They should then sort them into the top diagram on the worksheet and give each column a heading according to their criteria, using the word 'not' in the second column (for example, 'not wearing a skirt'). The children should then stick the pictures in the correct places. (NB: If there is insufficient space, let the children create their own diagram on a separate sheet of paper.) Next, they should think of another way of sorting the pictures, cut out a second set of pictures from the resource sheet and stick them into the second table provided on the worksheet 'Sorting diagrams (3)', again writing their own headings. Finally, they should think of a third set of criteria and make up a table (on a separate sheet of paper) that satisfies their criteria. Encourage the children to think of their own criteria but give prompts if they struggle (for example, boys and girls, long hair and not long hair, the different clothes).

Walk the line

Framework objective
Read the numbered divisions on a scale, and interpret the divisions between them; use a ruler to draw and measure lines to the nearest centimetre

Learning outcomes

- I can read numbers on a scale.
- I can use a ruler or metre stick to measure how long something is.
- I can read numbers on a scale and work out the numbers between them.
- I can read scales marked in fives and tens.

Give each child a copy of the worksheet 'Walk the line', and provide rulers and sharp pencils. Sit with the group of children you particularly wish to assess, asking them what they should do, and ensuring that they start measuring at the zero mark on the ruler.

Name Date

Sorting diagrams (1)

1. Tick all the children who are wearing bobble hats.

2. How many children are wearing bobble hats? ________

3. Complete the table to show how many children are wearing the items of clothing listed below.

Clothes	How many?
Wellies	
Scarves	
Bobble hats and wellies	

How easy?

Red
Amber
Green

How do you think you have done?

____

____

Name Date

Sorting diagrams (2)

■ Write these numbers in the correct places on the diagram below.

150	36	121	7
210	4	55	83
	72	17	

	Two-digit number	Not a two-digit number
Odd		
Not odd		

How easy?

Red
Amber
Green

How do you think you have done?

Name Date

Sorting diagrams (3)

- Cut out one set of the children from the resource sheet 'Sorting diagrams (4)'.
- Sort them into this diagram.
- Label each part of your diagram.

____________________	Not ____________________

- Cut out a second set of children.
- Use a different way to sort them into two lists.
- Label each list.

How easy?

How do you think you have done?

____

____

Name Date

Walk the line

1. Measure each line below.

2. Draw a line that is 8cm long.

How easy?

Red

Amber

Green

How do you think you have done?

BLOCK D

Calculating, measuring and understanding shape

Expected prior learning

Check that children can already:

- solve problems involving counting, adding or subtracting, doubling or halving
- use practical and informal written methods for addition and subtraction of a one-digit number or a multiple of 10 to and from a one- or two-digit number
- estimate, measure and compare objects, choosing suitable uniform non-standard or standard units and instruments
- use vocabulary related to time; order days of the week and months; read the time to the hour and half hour
- visualise and use everyday language to describe the position of objects and direction and distance when moving them.

Objectives overview

The text in this diagram identifies the focus of mathematics learning within the block.

Key aspects of learning

- Problem solving
- Reasoning
- Evaluation
- Social skills
- Communication

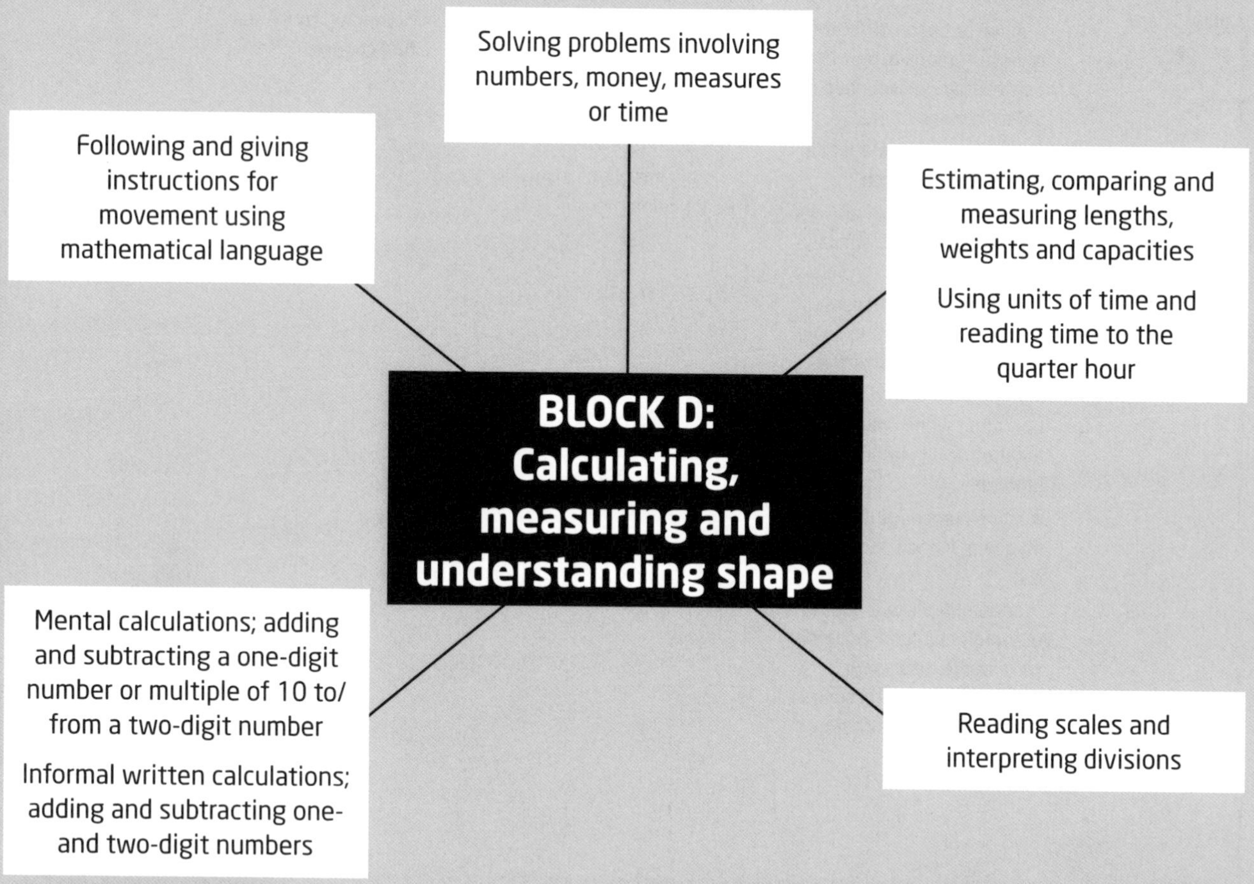

BLOCK D: Calculating, measuring and understanding shape

- Solving problems involving numbers, money, measures or time
- Following and giving instructions for movement using mathematical language
- Estimating, comparing and measuring lengths, weights and capacities
- Using units of time and reading time to the quarter hour
- Mental calculations; adding and subtracting a one-digit number or multiple of 10 to/from a two-digit number
- Informal written calculations; adding and subtracting one- and two-digit numbers
- Reading scales and interpreting divisions

Unit 1 Calculating, measuring and understanding shape

Introduction

In this unit, children count in ones, twos, fives and tens and use these skills to add mixed 10p, 5p, 2p and 1p coins. They use the mental skill of adding a single-digit number to a two-digit number and apply this to problem solving with money and measures. They position numbers on number lines or scales numbered in twos, fives or tens. They can use this skill to read simple scales on rulers, weighing scales and measuring jugs. They estimate, measure and compare lengths, weights and capacities. They tell the time to the hour and half hour. They follow and give instructions involving position and movement and can plot symbols on a labelled grid. Threaded throughout this entire block is the 'using and applying' objective of solving problems involving numbers, money, measures and time.

Framework objectives	Assessment focuses		Success criteria for Year 2	Learning outcomes
	Level 2	Level 1		
(1) **Coins**				
Solve problems involving addition, subtraction, multiplication or division in contexts of numbers, measures or pounds and pence	• select the mathematics they use in some classroom activities, e.g. with support • find a starting point, identifying key facts/relevant information • use apparatus, diagrams, role-play etc to represent and clarify a problem • move between different representations of a problem, e.g. a situation described in words, a diagram etc • adopt a suggested model or systematic approach • make connections and apply their knowledge to similar situations • use mathematical content from levels 1 and 2 to solve problems and investigate • choose the appropriate operation when solving addition and subtraction problems • solve number problems involving money and measures, e.g. • add/subtract two-digit and one-digit numbers, bridging tens where necessary in contexts using units such as pence, pounds, centimetres	• use mathematics as an integral part of classroom activities, e.g. with support • engage with practical mathematical activities involving sorting, counting and measuring by direct comparison • begin to understand the relevance of mathematical ideas to everyday situations by using them in role-play • solve addition/subtraction problems involving up to ten objects, e.g. • solve problems involving 1p or £1 coins	• can solve problems involving counting, adding or subtracting, doubling or halving • know the value of all coins and can exchange larger coins for equivalent smaller ones • can pay for items costing up to £1 and find change	*I can decide what calculation to do to solve a problem.*

BLOCK D

Unit 1 Calculating, measuring and understanding shape

Framework objectives	Assessment focuses: Level 2	Assessment focuses: Level 1	Success criteria for Year 2	Learning outcomes
(2) How many?				
Add or subtract mentally a single-digit number or a multiple of 10 to or from any two-digit number; use practical and informal written methods to add and subtract two-digit numbers	● use mental recall of addition and subtraction facts to 10, e.g. • use addition/subtraction facts to 10 and place value to add or subtract multiples of 10, e.g. know 3 + 7 = 10 and use place value to derive 30 + 70 = 100 ● use mental calculation strategies to solve number problems including those involving money and measures, e.g. • recall doubles to 10 + 10 and other significant doubles, e.g. double 50p is 100p or £1 • use knowledge of doubles to 10 + 10 to derive corresponding halves	● add and subtract numbers of objects to 10 • begin to add by counting on from the number of objects in the first set ● begin to know some addition facts, e.g. • doubles of numbers to double 5	● can relate addition to counting on and subtraction to counting either on or back ● know addition can be done in any order to give the same result, but that in subtraction if the order is changed the answer will be different ● can use practical and informal written methods	*I can add and subtract some numbers in my head.*
(3) Full or empty?				
Estimate, compare and measure lengths, weights and capacities, choosing and using standard units (m, cm, kg, litre) and suitable measuring instruments	● begin to use everyday non-standard and standard units to measure length and mass • begin to understand that numbers can be used not only to count discrete objects but also to describe continuous measures, e.g. length • know which measuring tools to use to find, for example, how much an object weighs, how tall a child is, how long it takes to run around the edge of the playground, how much water it takes to fill the water tray • read scales to the nearest labelled division • begin to make sensible estimates in relation to familiar units	● measure and order objects using direct comparison • compare lengths directly and put them in order • respond to and use the language of comparison: longer, longest, shorter, shortest, more, less, heavier, lighter • check which of two objects is heavier/lighter and begin to put three objects into order • find objects that are longer/shorter than a metre, heavier/lighter than 500 grams, hold more/less than 1 litre	● can understand the relationship between the size of the unit and the number of units needed for the measurement ● can estimate, measure and compare capacities and describe using the appropriate vocabulary ● can choose and use suitable measuring instruments	*I can measure out a litre of water.*

BLOCK D

Unit 1 Calculating, measuring and understanding shape

Framework objectives	Assessment focuses – Level 2	Assessment focuses – Level 1	Success criteria for Year 2	Learning outcomes
④ How heavy?				
Read the numbered divisions on a scale, and interpret the divisions between them (e.g. on a scale from 0 to 25 with intervals of 1 shown but only the divisions 0, 5, 10, 15 and 20 numbered); use a ruler to draw and measure lines to the nearest centimetre	● begin to use everyday non-standard and standard units to measure length and mass ● begin to understand that numbers can be used not only to count discrete objects but also to describe continuous measures, e.g. length ● know which measuring tools to use to find, for example, how much an object weighs, how tall a child is, how long it takes to run around the edge of the playground, how much water it takes to fill the water tray ● read scales to the nearest labelled division ● begin to make sensible estimates in relation to familiar units	● measure and order objects using direct comparison ● compare lengths directly and put them in order ● respond to and use the language of comparison: longer, longest, shorter, shortest, more, less, heavier, lighter ● check which of two objects is heavier/lighter and begin to put three objects into order ● find objects that are longer/shorter than a metre, heavier/lighter than 500 grams, hold more/less than 1 litre	● can choose and use suitable units to estimate, measure and compare amounts ● can use their calculation skills to respond to questions involving measurement	*I can read numbers on a scale.*
⑤ What's the time?				
Use units of time (seconds, minutes, hours, days) and know the relationships between them; read the time to the quarter-hour; identify time intervals, including those that cross the hour	● begin to use a wider range of measures ● use a time line to order daily events and ordinal numbers (first, second, third...) to describe the order of some regular events	● order events ● order everyday events and describe the sequence ● use the vocabulary of time including days of the week ● read the time on an analogue clock at the hour and begin to know the half hour	● can use the vocabulary of time ● can read time to the hour and half-hour on an analogue clock ● can use time lines or clocks to help them to respond to questions	*I can estimate how long an activity might take, then check using a timer.* *I can tell the time when it is something o'clock or half past the hour.*
⑥ Where is it?				
Follow and give instructions involving position, direction and movement	● describe the position of objects, e.g. ● use ordinal numbers (first, second, third...) to describe the position of objects in a row or when giving directions ● recognise and explain that a shape stays the same even when it is held up in different orientations	● use everyday language to describe positions of 2D and 3D shapes ● respond to and use positional language, e.g. behind, under, on top of, next to, in between... ● respond to and use directional language in talk about objects and movement, e.g. forwards, backwards, turn	● can visualise and use everyday language to describe position, direction and distance ● can describe the route through a simple maze	*I can follow and give instructions to mark a position on a grid.*

Activity ①

Prior learning
Children can solve problems involving counting, adding, subtracting, doubling or halving using practical and written methods. They understand coin values and can exchange larger coins for smaller ones.

Framework objective
Solve problems involving addition, subtraction, multiplication or division in contexts of numbers, measures or pounds and pence

Vocabulary
problem, solution, puzzle, pattern, method, sign, operation, symbol, number sentence, equation, mental calculation, written calculation, informal method, jottings, diagrams, pictures, images, coin, pound (£), pence, price, cost, pay, costs more/less, change, total, how much

Resources
Interactive activity: Coins
Resource sheet: Self-assessment
Classroom resources: toys (each labelled with a price up to £1), coins

① Coins

Work with a group of children. Show the toys and ask the children to read the prices. Now open the interactive activity 'Coins'. Hold up one of the toys. *What coins could you use to pay for this?* Invite children to drag and drop the correct coins on the screen. Next, ask them to show you a different way of paying. Invite children to pick two toys and total the prices, showing their answers with the coins on the screen. Ask them to explain how they knew what to do and to write the calculation. Repeat the activity, this time finding change from £1. Decide whether to use the self-assessment sheet for children to record their achievements and what they need to do next.

Teacher support
Less confident learners: Work with prices that are multiples of 5p to 50p.
More confident learners: Work with amounts to £5. Ask the children to find totals by adding three prices, finding change from whole pounds and from 50p.

Common misconceptions
Children do not recognise the value of coins.
Give each child some pennies. Ask them to count out ten and exchange them for a 10p coin. Repeat for 5p and 2p. Encourage children to find the total by adding 5p to the 10p and then 2p.

Children think that a sum of pennies is more than an equivalent coin because there are more pennies.
Put five pennies on the table. Ask the children to compare them with a 5p coin. *Are the pennies worth more, less, the same as the 5p coin?* Check by counting. Repeat with other coins.

Probing questions
- How could I pay for this toy using the fewest coins?
- This toy costs 65p. I only have 36p. How much more money do I need?
- How did you work that out?

Next steps
Support: Ask the children to make some price labels up to 50p for toys in the classroom. Once they have, ask them to find the correct coins that could be used to pay for them. Next, encourage them to find the total cost of two toys by counting the coins. See also Year 2 Block B Unit 1.
Extension: Ask children various problems such as: *Sam spent 35p. Freddie spent 26p more. How much did Freddie spend?* See also Year 2 Block D Unit 2.

BLOCK D

Activity 2

Prior learning

Children relate addition to counting on and subtraction to counting on or back. They use written methods to add or subtract a one-digit number or a multiple of 10 to or from a one-digit or two-digit number.

Framework objective

Add or subtract mentally a single-digit number or a multiple of 10 to or from any two-digit number; use practical and informal written methods to add or subtract two-digit numbers

Vocabulary

add, plus, sum, total, subtract, take away, minus, difference, inverse

Resources

Resource sheets: 0-100 number cards, 0-100 number lines, Self-assessment
Classroom resources: counters

2 How many?

Give the children a 0-100 number line. Shuffle the 0-100 number cards. Invite each child to pick a card. Ask the children to add and then subtract 8 from their number. Target particular children to describe how they did this - for example, partition 8 to get to the next multiple of 10 and then add the rest; add 10 and take off 2; count on. Repeat this for adding and subtracting multiples of 10. Decide whether to use the self-assessment sheet for children to record their achievements and what they need to do next.

Teacher support

Less confident learners: Use number cards to 40. Encourage the children to use one particular strategy to add 8 (for example, counting on).
More confident learners: Give the children calculations that involve additions or subtractions of any two-digit numbers. Observe which strategies they use.

Common misconceptions

Children count the first number as 1 when counting on or back.
Help the children by physically moving their fingers along a number line, counting correctly with them.

Children have difficulty partitioning single-digit numbers.
Give the children some counters (for example, nine). Ask them to make two piles with them in as many different ways as they can and to record what they have done in number sentences.

Probing questions

- What number facts could you use to add 27 and 9?
- How might partitioning help you to answer this question?
- Can you think of another way of answering this question?

Next steps

Support: To progress from counting in single numbers, help these children to develop the strategy of partitioning a number such as 8 to make the next multiple of 10. For example: 27 + 8 = 27 + 3 + 5. Provide counters to help. See also Year 2 Block B Unit 1.
Extension: Encourage the children to make up calculations that would be best solved using particular strategies such as partitioning, adding/subtracting a near multiple of 10 by adding/subtracting the multiple and adjusting, near doubles or bridging 10. See also Year 2 Block D Unit 2.

Activity 3

Prior learning
Children begin to understand the relationship between the size of the unit and the number of units needed. They can estimate, measure, compare and describe the length, weight and capacity of different objects.

Framework objective
Estimate, compare and measure lengths, weights and capacities, choosing and using standard units (m, cm, kg, litre) and suitable measuring instruments

Vocabulary
measuring scale, compare, measure, weigh, further, metre (m), centimetre (cm), tape measure, kilogram (kg), half-kilogram, gram (g), capacity, contains, litre (l), half-litre, millilitre (ml)

Resources
Resource sheet: Self-assessment
Classroom resources: measuring jug filled to 1 litre mark with water, containers and bottles with different capacities (2l, 1½l, 500cl and so on)

3 Full or empty?

Discuss the vocabulary of capacity, targeting the children you wish to assess to see if they know and understand the true meaning of the words. Give each group a selection of empty containers and bottles. Ask them to sort these into those that will hold about 1 litre, those that will hold more and those that will hold less. Observe groups as they undertake the task. Once they have sorted the containers, ask them to attempt to fill each container with 1 litre of water from a measuring jug to see if they were correct. Encourage them to compare their results with their estimates. Decide whether to use the self-assessment sheet for children to record their achievements and next steps.

Teacher support
Less confident learners: Provide three containers: 2 litres, 1 litre and a half-litre. Ask the children to estimate, measure and compare how much water each container will hold.
More confident learners: Ask these children to order their containers from least capacity to greatest. Encourage more precision in estimates (for example, 'between ¼ and ½ a litre', 'between ¾ and 1 litre').

Common misconception
Children cannot estimate capacity.
Give children practical experience by encouraging them to fill and empty pairs of containers, saying which contains the most and which the least. They should then compare these pairs with 1 litre of water in a measuring jug. Provide a range of containers of varying heights and shapes to illustrate that a tall container does not necessarily have a greater capacity than a short container.

Probing questions
- Do you think this container/bottle will hold 1 litre of water? Why do you think that?
- Do you think you will need to add water to this container to make 1 litre or pour some away? Why?

Next steps
Support: Ask the children to fill a measuring jug to half a litre and then 1 litre. Each time, pour the measured water into a 2-litre bottle and ask the children to compare the amount in the bottle to what it would be if it was full. See also Year 2 Block C Unit 1.
Extension: Ask the children to measure water more precisely into containers (for example, ½ litre, ¼ litre, ¾ litre, 1½ litres), and to label the containers with the amount held. See also Year 2 Block D Unit 2.

Activity 4

Prior learning
Children can use uniform non-standard units to estimate, measure and compare lengths, capacities and weight. They are beginning to use standard units.

Framework objective
Read the numbered divisions on a scale, and interpret the divisions between them; use a ruler to draw and measure lines to the nearest centimetre

Vocabulary
measuring scale, compare, measure, weigh, further, metre (m), centimetre (cm), tape measure, kilogram (kg), half-kilogram, gram (g), capacity, contains, litre (l), half-litre, millilitre (ml)

Resources
Interactive activity: How heavy?
Resource sheet: Self-assessment
Classroom resources: bunch of grapes (500g), carton of milk (500g), bread (600g), bag of flour (1kg), weighing scales

4 How heavy?

Work with a group. Reveal the interactive activity 'How heavy?'. Invite children to hold each item and compare it with the 1kg bag of flour. *Do you think it is heavier, lighter or the same?* Then they drag the picture of each item in turn onto the scales and compare the position of the needle to 1kg. Remind the children that the unmarked divisions show hundreds and ask individual children to read the weights. Repeat for the pictures of the potatoes (1kg 400g), orange juice (500g) and cheese (300g). Decide whether to use the self-assessment sheet for children to record their achievements and what they need to do next.

Teacher support
Less confident learners: Use the interactive activity 'How heavy?'. Invite children to drag and drop several items and say for each which whole kilogram they are closest to or halfway between.
More confident learners: Drag and drop several items and ask the children to read the total weight on the scale.

Common misconceptions
Children cannot estimate weight.
Give children plenty of practical experience by encouraging them to compare different items by holding them in one hand and a 1kg bag of sugar in the other. Sort the items into those that weigh more, less or about the same as 1kg.

Children cannot read the scale on weighing scales of the interactive activity.
Provide weighing scales. Place different items on them and ask children to point at the needle and tell you which whole kilogram the weight is closest to.

Probing questions
- What measurement is this? How do you know?
- Which whole kilogram is this weight closest to?
- If I put an item on the scales and the pointer is here, how heavy is it?

Next steps
Support: Give the children different items to weigh on a set of scales and say whether each is more or less than a kilogram. Encourage them to estimate first and then check, and to record their findings in a simple diagram that you prepare for them. See also Year 2 Block C Unit 1.
Extension: Give children the opportunity to measure different items on a set of weighing scales. Discuss the divisions on the scale and encourage them to read the measurements to the nearest 100 grams. See also Year 2 Block D Unit 2.

Activitiy 5

Prior learning

Children can read time to the hour and half-hour on an analogue clock and recognise half-past the hour in day-to-day routines. They can order the days of the week and months of the year.

Framework objective

Use units of time (seconds, minutes, hours, days) and know the relationships between them; read the time to the quarter-hour; identify time intervals, including those that cross the hour

Vocabulary

time, clock, watch, digital, analogue, hours (h), minutes (min), seconds (s), quarter to, quarter past

Resources

Interactive activity: What's the time?
Resource sheets: Self-assessment, Clock faces
Classroom resources: clocks with moveable hands (one clock per child)

5 What's the time?

Open the interactive activity 'What's the time?'. *What does each clock hand show?* Show two o'clock and ask the children to show the same time on their clocks. *I am going out in two hours. Show me that time on your clock.* Repeat for intervals involving 'half past': *Clare went out at three o'clock. She came back one and a half hours later.* Invite those you want to assess to show the time on the interactive tool. Decide whether to use the self-assessment sheet for children to record their achievements and what they need to do next.

Teacher support

Less confident learners: Concentrate on 'o'clock' times, asking questions such as: *I am going out at seven o'clock. Show the time on your clock.*
More confident learners: Once the children have shown that they are confident with 'o'clock' and 'half past' times, ask them to find 'quarter past' and 'quarter to' times on their clocks.

Common misconception

Children do not understand the concept of 'half past'.
Remind children of the idea of 'half' in other situations (for example, cakes, shapes, sets of beads). Provide the resource sheet 'Clock faces' and ask children to colour each half a different colour. Make the link between 'half past' and half turns in position by asking children to face one wall and make a half turn. Then demonstrate a half turn on a clock face from an o'clock time to half past the hour and half past to o'clock – for example, from four o'clock to half past four, and from half past four to five o'clock.

Probing questions

- How many minutes are there in an hour?
- What about half an hour? How do you know?
- If it is half past six, how many minutes past six o'clock is that?

Next steps

Support: During oral and mental starter activities, give regular opportunities for the children to tell you half-past and o'clock times and show them on clocks. See also Year 1 Block D Unit 3.
Extension: Provide opportunities to convert analogue times to digital. Use the interactive activity 'What's the time?' to demonstrate o'clock and half-past times. See also Year 2 Block D Unit 2.

BLOCK D

Activity 6

Prior learning

Children can describe the position of objects and direction and distance when moving them. They can use the directions 'right', 'left' and 'straight on' to describe a route.

Framework objective

Follow and give instructions involving position, direction and movement

Vocabulary

direction, route, clockwise, anti-clockwise, quarter turn, right angle, straight line

Resources

Display page: Where is it?
Worksheet: Where is it?
Classroom resources: whiteboards and pens, plastic shapes

6 Where is it?

Reveal the display page 'Where is it?'. Draw a cross in square C2 and ask the children to identify its position, writing it on their whiteboards. Repeat this by drawing symbols in different positions. Invite those you particularly wish to assess to draw symbols in squares that you name, such as D1. Provide each child with a copy of the worksheet 'Where is it?' and ask them to draw symbols in different positions. Then, working in pairs, have them take it in turns to describe the position of each symbol for their partner to draw on their own grid.

Teacher support

Less confident learners: Ask the children to put crosses on the worksheet 'Where is it?' as you put them on the interactive screen.
More confident learners: Ask these children to draw a circle in D3, then a cross in the square that is two to the right, a triangle in the square that is one down (and so on).

Common misconceptions

Children do not say the letter first and then the number when giving position.
Encourage these children to learn a simple phrase to help them remember the standard order that the coordinates are given, such as: *Along the corridor and up the stairs.*

Children cannot plot points correctly on a grid.
Encourage these children to use their fingers or a ruler to help them to find the correct place to position their symbol, always finding the letter on the horizontal axis first.

Probing questions

- Where is this cross? How do you know?
- If I put a circle one square to the left, where will it go?
- Where can I draw a circle?

Next steps

Support: Give the children a large labelled grid and some shapes. Ask them to place the shapes in different places and to record where they are. See also Year 1 Block D Unit 3.
Extension: Give the children the opportunity to make a treasure map on a larger grid and to make up instructions to find the treasure. Repeat this for other items on the grid, such as trees, pond. See also Year 2 Block D Unit 2.

Unit 2  Calculating, measuring and understanding shape

Introduction

In this unit, children add or subtract multiples of 10, find the sum or difference of one- and two-digit numbers and use a range of calculation strategies such as doubling or halving. They use these skills to solve one and two step problems involving money and measures. They estimate, measure and compare lengths, weights and capacities, reading a scale to the nearest division in order to do this. They give instructions involving position, direction and movement including whole, half and quarter turns. They use this skill to help them tell the time to the quarter hour and find these times on both analogue and digital clocks.

Framework objectives	Assessment focuses		Success criteria for Year 2	Learning outcomes
	Level 2	Level 1		
(1) Problems, problems				
Solve problems involving addition, subtraction, multiplication or division in contexts of numbers, measures or pounds and pence	• select the mathematics they use in some classroom activities, e.g. with support • find a starting point, identifying key facts/relevant information • use apparatus, diagrams, role-play etc to represent and clarify a problem • adopt a suggested model or systematic approach • make connections and apply their knowledge to similar situations • choose the appropriate operation when solving addition and subtraction problems • solve number problems with money and measures, e.g. • add/subtract two-digit and one-digit numbers, bridging tens where necessary in contexts using units such as pence, pounds, centimetres	• use mathematics as an integral part of classroom activities, e.g. with support • engage with practical mathematical activities involving sorting, counting and measuring by direct comparison • begin to understand the relevance of mathematical ideas to everyday situations by using them in role-play • solve addition/subtraction problems involving up to ten objects, e.g. • solve problems involving 1p or £1 coins	• can count in ones, twos, fives and tens and use these skills to help them calculate • can apply calculation skills to solving word problems, deciding which calculation to use, justifying their decisions and checking their answers	*I can decide what calculation to do to solve a problem.*
(2) Which strategy?				
Add or subtract mentally a one-digit number or a multiple of 10 to or from any two-digit number; use practical and informal written methods to add or subtract two-digit numbers	• use mental recall of addition and subtraction facts to 10 • use mental calculation strategies to solve number problems including those of money and measures, e.g. • recall doubles to 10 + 10 and other significant doubles, e.g. double 50p is 100p or £1 • use knowledge of doubles to 10 + 10 to derive corresponding halves	• add and subtract numbers of objects to 10 • begin to add by counting on from the number of objects in the first set • begin to know some addition facts, e.g. • doubles of numbers to double 5	• can use mental strategies to add or subtract mentally • can use number squares to add or subtract • can use number facts to partition • can transfer these skills from the context of number and apply them in order to solve problems	*I can add and subtract some numbers in my head.* *I can add and subtract bigger numbers using practical equipment or written notes to help me.*

BLOCK D

Unit 2 Calculating, measuring and understanding shape

Framework objectives	Assessment focuses Level 2	Assessment focuses Level 1	Success criteria for Year 2	Learning outcomes
3 How many centimetres?				
Estimate, compare and measure lengths, weights and capacities, choosing and using standard units (m, cm, kg, litre) and suitable measuring instruments	• begin to use everyday non-standard and standard units to measure length and mass • know which measuring tools to use to find, for example, how much an object weighs, how tall a child is, how long it takes to run around the edge of the playground, how much water it takes to fill the water tray • read scales to the nearest labelled division • begin to make sensible estimates in relation to familiar units	• measure and order objects using direct comparison • compare lengths directly and put them in order • respond to and use the language of comparison: longer, longest, shorter, shortest, more, less, heavier, lighter • check which of two objects is heavier/lighter and begin to put three objects into order • find objects that are longer/shorter than a metre, heavier/lighter than 500 grams, hold more/less than 1 litre	• can estimate, measure and compare lengths • can estimate how long a piece of string is and then measure it with a ruler • can measure using centimetres	*I can estimate length in centimetres.* *I can estimate length in metres.* *I can decide whether it is better to use centimetres or metres for measuring different lengths.*
4 How full?				
Read the numbered divisions on a scale, and interpret the divisions between them (e.g. on a scale from 0 to 25 with intervals of 1 shown but only the divisions 0, 5, 10, 15 and 20 numbered); use a ruler to draw and measure lines to the nearest centimetre	• begin to use everyday non-standard and standard units to measure length and mass • begin to understand that numbers can be used not only to count discrete objects but also to describe continuous measures, e.g. length • know which measuring tools to use to find, for example, how much an object weighs, how tall a child is, how long it takes to run around the edge of the playground etc • read scales to the nearest labelled division	• measure and order objects using direct comparison • compare lengths directly and put them in order • respond to and use the language of comparison: longer, longest, shorter, shortest, more, less, heavier, lighter • check which of two objects is heavier/lighter and begin to put three objects into order • find objects that are longer/shorter than a metre, heavier/lighter than 500 grams, hold more/less than 1 litre	• can position numbers on a scale numbered in twos, fives or tens • can measure capacities to the nearest half litre	*I can read numbers on a scale and work out the numbers between them.*
5 Quarter of an hour				
Use units of time (seconds, minutes, hours, days) and know the relationships between them; read the time to the quarter-hour; identify time intervals, including those that cross the hour	• begin to use a wider range of measures • make and use a 'right-angle checker' • use a time line to order daily events and ordinal numbers (first, second, third...) to describe the order of some regular events	• order events • order everyday events and describe the sequence • use the vocabulary of time including days of the week • read the time on an analogue clock at the hour and begin to know the half hour	• knows there are 60 seconds in a minute • can estimate and time how long activities take • can read the time on an analogue clock to the nearest quarter-hour.	*I know that one hour is the same as 60 minutes.* *I can tell the time when it is quarter past, half past or quarter to the hour.* *I know that quarter past three is the same time as three fifteen.*

BLOCK D

Unit 2 Calculating, measuring and understanding shape

Framework objectives	Assessment focuses: Level 2	Assessment focuses: Level 1	Success criteria for Year 2	Learning outcomes
6 Round we go				
Recognise and use whole, half and quarter turns, both clockwise and anticlockwise; know that a right angle represents a quarter turn	• understand angle as a measurement of turn • describe the position of objects, e.g. • use ordinal numbers (first, second...) to describe the position of objects in a row or when giving directions • recognise and explain that a shape stays the same even when it is held up in different orientations • begin to use a wider range of measures	• use everyday language to describe positions of 2D and 3D shapes • respond to and use positional language, e.g. behind, under, on top of, next to, in between... • respond to and use directional language in talk about objects and movement, e.g. forwards, backwards, turn	• can visualise and use everyday language to describe direction • knows the directions of right, left and straight on • can follow and give instructions to make whole, half and quarter turns in any direction	*In PE I can turn on the spot through whole, half or quarter turns, either clockwise or anticlockwise.*
7 Find it!				
Follow and give instructions involving position, direction and movement	• distinguish between straight and turning movements • distinguish between left and right and between clockwise and anticlockwise, and use these when giving directions • instruct a programmable robot, combining straight-line movements and turns, to move along a defined path or reach a target destination	• use everyday language to describe positions of 2D and 3D shapes • respond to and use positional language, e.g. behind, under, on top of, next to, in between... • respond to and use directional language in talk about objects and movement, e.g. forwards, backwards, turn	• can follow and give directions • can find symbols plotted on a grid using simple coordinates, remembering that the letters on the horizontal axis are said first • can give instructions for a partner to follow	*I can make a floor robot follow a path marked out on the floor.* *I can estimate the number of robot steps that the robot must take to reach the traffic cone.*

BLOCK D

Activity 1

Prior learning
Children can count in ones, twos, fives and tens and add mixed coins up to and including 10p. They can apply calculation skills to calculate, justify and solve word problems involving money and measures.

Framework objective
Solve problems involving addition, subtraction, multiplication or division in contexts of numbers, measures or pounds and pence

Vocabulary
problem, solution, puzzle, pattern, method, sign, operation, symbol, number sentence, equation, mental calculation, written calculation, informal method, jottings, diagrams, pictures, images, coin, pound (£), pence, price, cost, pay, costs more/less, change, total, how much

Resources
Resource sheets: Problems, problems (cut out cards for each group), Self-assessment
Classroom resources: number lines, counting objects

1 Problems, problems

Work with a group. Shuffle the problem cards cut from the resource sheet 'Problems, problems'. The children pick a card and read the problem aloud. They then decide what the question is asking and which calculation to do. They answer the question, consider if their answer is sensible, then check it using the inverse operation or an alternative strategy. Discuss how they do this with the particular children you wish to assess. Provide number lines and practical equipment for them to use should they choose to. Decide whether to use the self-assessment sheet for children to record their achievements and what they need to do next.

Teacher support
Less confident learners: Use the activities on the resource sheet 'Problems, problems' but change the numbers so they are within the range the children can work with confidently. Provide support with calculating.
More confident learners: Set word problems similar to those on 'Problems, problems', but make the numbers more challenging.

Common misconception
Children do not understand how to work through a problem.
With the children, work through the problem-solving steps to find out what the question is and to identify the relevant information. Together discuss what they need to do with the information to get the answer. Write down the information for them if necessary, and invite children to say what calculation is needed and why.

Probing questions
- I have 20 counters. I am going to give you a quarter of them. How many will I give you?
- What calculation will you need to do to work that out?
- How can you check?

Next steps
Support: Concentrate on one-step problems. Remind the children of the problem-solving steps: read and identify the question; decide where to start; follow a plan; review and choose next move; solve; and check your answer. See also Year 2 Block D Unit 1.
Extension: Give the children more two-step problems to solve rather than single-step problems. Ensure that they cover all four operations and allow for a variety of strategies. See also Year 2 Block D Unit 3.

Activity 2

Prior learning
Children can add or subtract single-digit numbers to or from two-digit numbers, bridging through a multiple of 10. They can use number squares to add or subtract a multiple of 10 and number facts to partition the number.

Framework objective

Add or subtract mentally a single-digit number or a multiple of ten to or from any two-digit number; use practical and informal written methods to add and subtract two-digit numbers

Vocabulary

add, plus, sum, total, subtract, take away, minus, difference, inverse

Resources

Display page: Which strategy?
Resource sheets: 0-100 number cards, Self-assessment
Classroom resources: 100-squares, number lines, place value equipment, counting objects

2 Which strategy?

Reveal the display page 'Which strategy?'. Shuffle the number cards and ask two children to pick one each. Write the numbers in the first calculation on the screen – for example, 34 + 29. Ask the children to find the answer. Let them use 100-squares, number lines and practical equipment if they require them. They should record their methods. Encourage them to consider such strategies as near doubles, partitioning, bridging 10, adding a near multiple of 10 and adjusting. Ask individual children you wish to assess to explain how they worked. Decide whether to use the self-assessment sheet for children to record their achievements and what they need to do next.

Teacher support

Less confident learners: Give these children single-digit numbers to add or subtract to or from a two-digit number. Encourage them to use one strategy (for example, bridging 10).
More confident learners: Encourage these children to solve the calculations by using two different strategies. Discuss the strategies used. Ask: *Which is the most efficient?*

Common misconception

Children lack confidence when bridging 10.
Give children a list of number pairs to 10, ie 1 + 9 = 10, 2 + 8 = 10 (and so on). Write this calculation: 26 + 7. Give the children seven counters. Ask: *What is the units digit in 26?* (6) They look on their list to see what would need to be added to give 10. Agree on 4, and take four counters from the seven, asking how many are left. Then write: 26 + 7 = 26 + 4 + 3 = 30 + 3 = 33.

Probing questions

- How could I add 45 and 39? Can you think of another way?
- How might doubling help?

Next steps

Support: Develop one particular strategy, such as adding a near multiple of 10 and adjusting. Encourage the children to use a number line to help them. For example, for 26 + 19, recognise that 19 is 1 less than 20; count on 20 by drawing loops to 36 and 46, and then move back 1 to 45. See also Year 2 Block D Unit 1.
Extension: Encourage the children to consider several strategies when calculating – for example, partitioning, adding/subtracting near multiple of 10 (adding/subtracting the multiple and adjusting), near doubles, and bridging 10. See also Year 2 Block D Unit 3.

Activity 3

Prior learning
Children can estimate, measure and compare lengths, weights and capacities. They are beginning to measure using centimetres, grams and millilitres.

Framework objective
Estimate, compare and measure lengths, weights and capacities, choosing and using standard units (m, cm, kg, litre) and suitable measuring instruments

Vocabulary
measuring scale, compare, measure, weigh, further, metre (m), centimetre (cm), tape measure, kilogram (kg), half-kilogram, gram (g), capacity, contains, litre (l), half-litre, millilitre (ml)

Resources
Resource sheet: Self-assessment
Classroom resources: six different lengths of string in multiples of 5cm from 5cm to 1.5m, rulers, metre sticks

3 How many centimetres?

Work with a group. *How many centimetres are there in one metre? ...half a metre? ...two metres?* Give the group the lengths of string. *Which strings will you measure with a ruler and which with a metre stick? Why?* Ask the children to order the strings from shortest to longest and then to group them into piles, one for those they think are shorter than a 30cm ruler and one for those they think are longer. Next, ask them to estimate the length of each string, then measure them to see how accurate their estimates were. Decide whether to use the self-assessment sheet for children to record their achievements and what they need to do next.

Teacher support
Less confident learners: Give the children four lengths of string with lengths in multiples of 10cm.
More confident learners: Ask these children to cut extra pieces of string with lengths between those of the given pieces, and that are not multiples of 5cm. Encourage them to measure each to the nearest centimetre.

Common misconception
Children cannot estimate length.
Give children plenty of practical experience by encouraging them to draw lines with lengths 10cm, 20cm and 30cm. Then ask them to draw other lines that are close/not close to these measurements and compare them, using words such as 'shorter than', 'longer than', 'nearly'. (Check that they start at the zero mark on their rulers.)

Probing questions
- How long do you think this pencil is?
- What did you do to help you estimate?
- How can you check your estimate?

Next steps
Support: Ask the children to draw lines of particular lengths onto plain paper and give them to a friend. The friend then estimates each length, writes down their estimate, then measures and labels each line with the correct length. See also Year 2 Block D Unit 1.
Extension: Ask the children to draw lines of random length on plain paper and give them to a partner who estimates the lengths then measures them to the nearest centimetre. They swap papers again and check each other's measuring. See also Year 2 Block D Unit 3.

Activity 4

Prior learning

Children can position numbers on a scale numbered in twos, five or tens. They can read a measurement to the nearest centimetre on a metre stick numbered in 10cm intervals. They can measure weights to the nearest half-kilogram and capacities to the nearest half-litre.

Framework objective

Read the numbered divisions on a scale, and interpret the divisions between them (e.g. on a scale from 0 to 25 with intervals of 1 shown but only the divisions 0, 5, 10, 15 and 20 numbered); use a ruler to draw and measure lines to the nearest centimetre

Vocabulary

measuring scale, compare, measure, weigh, further, metre (m), centimetre (cm), tape measure, kilogram (kg), half-kilogram, gram (g), capacity, contains, litre (l), half-litre, millilitre (ml)

Resources

Interactive activity: How full?
Resource sheet: Self-assessment
Classroom resources: whiteboards and pens, measuring jugs and other containers, water

4 How full?

Work with a group. Reveal the interactive activity 'How full?'. Ask the children to explain the scale. (It goes up in 100ml steps and ten of these make 1000ml, which is the same as 1 litre.) Fill the jug to different levels (for example, 300ml, 700ml, 900ml) and ask the children to write the amounts on their whiteboards. Next, empty some liquid and ask them how much has gone. Repeat this process for amounts halfway between divisions and ask them to estimate the new levels. Decide whether to use the self-assessment sheet for children to record their achievements and what they need to do next.

Teacher support

Less confident learners: Ask the children to say which 100ml amount the level is closest to or halfway between.
More confident learners: Fill the jug to different levels between the 100ml intervals and ask the children to estimate the level, then to read the scale.

Common misconception

Children cannot read the scale on a measuring jug.
Use the interactive activity 'How full?'. Fill the measuring jug to numbered divisions for children to read, reminding them that the scale is like a number line.

Probing questions

- What measurement is this? How do you know?
- Which 100ml is the liquid closest to?
- If I fill the jug to here, how much liquid will there be?

Next steps

Support: Give the children the opportunity to practically measure to the nearest half-litre, using a variety of containers and a measuring jug. Encourage them to estimate first and then check, and to record their findings. See also Year 2 Block D Unit 1.
Extension: Give the children the opportunity to measure different amounts of water into containers, using a measuring jug. They fill the jug to specified levels that involve measuring to the nearest 50ml. Discuss the divisions on the scale with them first. See also Year 2 Block D Unit 3.

BLOCK D

Activity 5

Prior learning
Children can use minutes and seconds. They know there are 60 seconds in one minute. They can read the time to the hour and half-hour on an analogue clock.

Framework objective
Use units of time (seconds, minutes, hours, days) and know the relationships between them; read the time to the quarter-hour; identify time intervals, including those that cross the hour

Vocabulary
time, clock, watch, digital, analogue, hours (h), minutes (min), seconds (s), quarter to, quarter past

Resources
Interactive activity: Quarter of an hour
Resource sheets: Clock faces, Self-assessment
Classroom resources: clocks with moveable hands (one per child)

5 Quarter of an hour

Reveal the interactive activity 'Quarter of an hour'. Say or write on the board 'quarter past seven' and ask the children to show this time on their clocks. Discuss what each hand represents and where they are positioned. *How would we show this on the digital clock? Why is 15 in the minutes position?* Ask them to show different times to the quarter-hour on their clocks. Invite children to show analogue and digital times on the screen. Decide whether to use the self-assessment sheet for children to record their achievements and what they need to do next.

Teacher support
Less confident learners: Concentrate on analogue and digital 'o'clock' and 'half past' times. Ask the children to show specific times and write them digitally.
More confident learners: Provide the resource sheet 'Clock faces'. Ask the children to draw 'o'clock', 'half past', 'quarter to' and 'quarter past' times and also to write the times digitally.

Common misconception
Children do not understand the concept of 'quarter past' and 'quarter to'.
Remind children of quarters in other situations (for example, cakes). Provide the resource sheet 'Clock faces' and ask children to colour each quarter of a face a different colour. Make the link between 'quarter past' and 'quarter to' with quarter turns by asking children to face one wall and make a quarter turn to the right. Turn clock hands from four o'clock to quarter past, half past, quarter to five, and to five o'clock.

Probing questions
- How many seconds are there in a minute?
- What would quarter past three look like on a digital clock?
- If it is 2:15, what time will it be in half an hour?

Next steps
Support: During oral and mental starter activities, give regular opportunities for the children to tell you times and show them on clocks. See also Year 2 Block D Unit 1.
Extension: Once children are confident with showing and reading o'clock, half past, quarter to and quarter past on analogue and digital clocks, ask them to make up and solve problems. For example: *I went to the library at quarter to 9, and stayed for 45 minutes. When did I leave?* See also Year 2 Block D Unit 3.

BLOCK D

Activity 6

Prior learning
Children can describe the position of objects and direction and distance when moving them. They know the directions of right, left and straight on and can give instructions to make whole, half and quarter turns.

Framework objective
Recognise and use whole, half and quarter turns, both clockwise and anticlockwise; know that a right angle represents a quarter turn

Vocabulary
direction, route, clockwise, anticlockwise, quarter turn, right angle, straight line

Resources
Resource sheet: Self-assessment
Classroom resources: two differently-coloured pieces of card, large analogue clock, compasses

 Round we go

Observe the children you wish to assess as you do this activity with the whole class. Begin by checking their knowledge of the vocabulary 'clockwise', 'anticlockwise', 'quarter turn', 'right angle', 'straight line'. Ask them to make up sentences using these words. Discuss how these turns relate to movements on a clock and how a quarter turn is a right angle. Ask the children to identify right angles in the classroom. In the hall or an open space, ask them to make different turns. You could hold up different-coloured paper to represent direction of turn and call out the size. Decide whether to use the self-assessment sheet for children to record their achievements and what they need to do next.

Teacher support
Less confident learners: Concentrate on the direction of turn so that the children become familiar with clockwise and anticlockwise. Ask them to make half turns in these directions.
More confident learners: Link this to the compass points of north, south, east and west, and practise turning in these directions.

Common misconceptions
Children do not recognise quarter turns or how to make them.
Give plenty of practice at turning and link this with the clock work the children have done, showing the minute hand moving from o'clock to quarter past.

Children do not remember which direction is clockwise and which anticlockwise.
Give children a clock face and remind them that the hands move clockwise. Draw arrows on a circle: one colour for clockwise and another for anticlockwise. Ask them to turn in a particular direction (for example, 'clockwise') and hold up that colour for children to see.

Probing questions
- Look at this shape. Close your eyes. Open your eyes again. I have turned the shape. What did I do to it? How can I get it back to where it was at the beginning?
- How would you move to face the door?

Next steps
Support: To reinforce and consolidate, use opportunities during PE to practise making whole, half- and quarter-sized turns. See also Year 1 Block D Unit 3.
Extension: Provide opportunities for the children to use a compass to make turns to the north, south, east and west. They should think of ways to describe their moves (for example, whole, half, quarter turns; clockwise and anticlockwise). See also Year 2 Block D Unit 3.

Activity 7

Prior learning

Children can give directions involving position and movement. They can find simple coordinates on a grid, remembering that the letters on the horizontal axis are given first in a coordinate pair.

Framework objective

Follow and give instructions involving position, direction and movement

Vocabulary

direction, route, clockwise, anticlockwise, quarter turn, right angle, straight line

Resources

Display page: Find it!
Worksheet: Find it!
Resource sheet: 5 × 5 grid

7 Find it!

Reveal the display page 'Find it!'. Use the pen tool to draw a simple robot in F9. Ask: *What is the robot's position?* Repeat for robots in different positions. Invite particular children to draw robots in given squares (for example, H8). Draw a cone in B3, and invite the children to tell you how they would direct the robot in F9 to the cone. Provide each child with the worksheet 'Find it!' and ask them to draw robots and cones in different positions. Then, working in pairs, they take it in turns to describe the position of each robot and its route to a cone for their partner to draw on their own grid.

Teacher support

Less confident learners: Give the children the resource sheet '5 × 5 grid'. Ask them to place circles in different squares and list the positions beside the grid.
More confident learners: Ask these children to write instructions for how to get from one symbol to another on their grids - for example, 2 left and 3 up.

Common misconception

Children cannot work out a route on a grid.
Encourage children to use a ruler to draw horizontal and vertical lines to help them work out the route from one square to another. For example, the route from B2 to H5 can be described as 6 right and 3 up.

Probing questions

- Where is this robot? How do you know?
- How can I get the robot to the cone?
- How many squares do you think it will be?

Next steps

Support: Ask the children to make a treasure map (or similar) on the resource sheet '5 × 5 grid'. They should plot the treasure chest, a pond and some trees, and give the positions for these items. They could then make up instructions for how to get to the treasure. See also Year 2 Block D Unit 1.
Extension: Give the children opportunities to look at and locate different places using simple grid references. See also Year 3 Block D Unit 1.

Unit 3  Calculating, measuring and understanding shape

Introduction

These lessons build on work carried out more extensively in Block C. Children add or subtract mentally a one-digit number or multiple of 10 to or from a two-digit number and using a range of calculation strategies. They use these skills to solve word problems involving money and measures using practical resources where helpful. They solve practical problems involving measures which entail estimating, measuring and checking. They recognise whole, half and quarter turns and continue to describe them and give instructions for following them. They make and draw quarter turns. They read the time to the quarter hour on analogue and digital clocks and find time intervals. Threaded throughout this entire unit is the 'using and applying' objective of solving problems involving numbers, money, measures and time.

Framework objectives	Assessment focuses		Success criteria for Year 2	Learning outcomes
	Level 2	Level 1		
(1) Money, money, money				
Solve problems involving addition, subtraction, multiplication or division in contexts of numbers, measures or pounds and pence	• select the mathematics they use in some classroom activities, e.g. with support • find a starting point, identifying key facts/relevant information • use apparatus, diagrams, role play etc to represent and clarify a problem • move between different representations of a problem e.g. a situation described in words, a diagram etc • adopt a suggested model or systematic approach • make connections and apply their knowledge to similar situations • use mathematical content from levels 1 and 2 to solve problems and investigate	• use mathematics as an integral part of classroom activities, e.g. with support • engage with practical mathematical activities involving sorting, counting and measuring by direct comparison • begin to understand the relevance of mathematical ideas to everyday situations by using them in role-play	• can answer problems that involve finding change and know that this is linked to subtraction • can use a range of calculation strategies to solve one-step and two-step problems involving money and measures • can use informal recording, pictures and diagrams where appropriate to support their calculations	*I can decide what calculations to do to solve a two-step word problem.*

BLOCK D

Unit 3 Calculating, measuring and understanding shape

Framework objectives	Assessment focuses: Level 2	Assessment focuses: Level 1	Success criteria for Year 2	Learning outcomes
(2) Totals and differences				
Add or subtract mentally a one-digit number or a multiple of 10 to or from any two-digit number; use practical and informal written methods to add and subtract two-digit numbers	• use mental recall of addition and subtraction facts to 10, e.g. • use addition/subtraction facts to 10 and place value to add or subtract multiples of 10, e.g. know 3 + 7 = 10 and use place value to derive 30 + 70 = 100 • use mental calculation strategies to solve number problems including those involving money and measures, e.g. • recall doubles to 10 + 10 and other significant doubles, e.g. double 50p is 100p or £1 • use knowledge of doubles to 10 + 10 to derive corresponding halves	• add or subtract numbers of objects to 10 • begin to add by counting on from the number of objects in the first set • begin to know some addition facts e.g. • doubles of numbers to double 5	• can add or subtract multiples of 10 • can find the sum or difference of single-digit and two-digit numbers and use doubling and halving • can add or subtract pairs of two-digit numbers using a variety of strategies • can use practical equipment, drawings diagrams or written notes to support them	*I can add and subtract bigger numbers using practical equipment or written notes to help me.*
(3) Weight				
Estimate, compare and measure lengths, weights and capacities, choosing and using standard units (m, cm, kg, litre) and suitable measuring instruments	• begin to use everyday non-standard and standard units to measure length and mass • begin to understand that numbers can be used not only to count discrete objects but also to describe continuous measures, e.g. length • know which measuring tools to use to find, for example, how much an object weighs, how tall a child is, how long it takes to run around the edge of the playground, how much water it takes to fill the water tray • read scales to the nearest labelled division • begin to make sensible estimates in relation to familiar units	• measure and order objects using direct comparison • compare lengths directly and put them in order • respond to and use the language of comparison: longer, longest, shorter, shortest, more, less, heavier, lighter • check which of two objects is heavier/lighter and begin to put three objects into order • find objects that are longer/shorter than a metre, heavier/lighter than 500 grams, hold more/less than one litre	• can estimate with increasing accuracy • can check estimates using a set of scales	*I know that a kilogram is 1000 grams.*

BLOCK D

Unit 3 Calculating, measuring and understanding shape

Framework objectives	Assessment focuses		Success criteria for Year 2	Learning outcomes
	Level 2	Level 1		
4 Draw the line				
Read the numbered divisions on a scale, and interpret the divisions between them (e.g. on a scale from 0 to 25 with intervals of 1 shown but only the divisions 0, 5, 10, 15 and 20 numbered); use a ruler to draw and measure lines to the nearest centimetre	• begin to use everyday non-standard and standard units to measure length and mass • begin to understand that numbers can be used not only to count discrete objects but also to describe continuous measures, e.g. length • know which measuring tools to use to find, for example, how much an object weighs, how tall a child is, how long it takes to run around the edge of the playground, how much water it takes to fill the water tray • read scales to the nearest labelled division • begin to make sensible estimates in relation to familiar units	• measure and order objects using direct comparison • compare lengths directly and put them in order • respond to and use the language of comparison: longer, longest, shorter, shortest, more, less, heavier, lighter • check which of two objects is heavier/lighter and begin to put three objects into order • find objects that are longer/shorter than a metre, heavier/lighter than 500 grams, hold more/less than one litre	• can read a scale to the nearest division • can use a ruler to draw lines and measure to the nearest centimetre	*I can read scales marked in twos, fives or tens.* *I can measure and draw lines to the nearest centimetre.*
5 Give me five!				
Use units of time (seconds, minutes, hours, days) and know the relationships between them; read the time to the quarter-hour; identify time intervals, including those that cross the hour	• begin to use a wider range of measures • use a time line to order daily events and ordinal numbers (first, second, third...) to describe the order of some regular events	• order events • order everyday events and describe the sequence • use the vocabulary of time including days of the week • read the time on an analogue clock at the hour and begin to know the half hour	• can tell the time to a quarter of an hour • knows that a quarter of an hour is 15 minutes • knows marked divisions go round in fives • can read o'clock, half past, quarter to and quarter past times using the digital vocabulary	*I know that there are 24 hours in a day.* *I can use a clock face to help me to count in steps of five minutes.*
6 Right angles				
Recognise and use whole, half and quarter turns, both clockwise and anticlockwise; know that a right angle represents a quarter turn	• understand angle as a measurement of turn • make whole turns, half turns and quarter turns • describe the position of objects, e.g. • use ordinal numbers (first, second, third...) to describe the position of objects in a row or when giving directions • recognise and explain that a shape stays the same even when it is held up in different orientations • recognise right angles in turns	• use everyday language to describe positions of 2D and 3D shapes • respond to and use positional language, e.g. behind, under, on top of, next to, in between... • respond to and use directional language in talk about objects and movement, e.g. forwards, backwards, turn	• can give instructions involving position, direction and movement using whole, half and quarter turns in clockwise and anticlockwise directions • recognise that a quarter turn produces a right angle and is the same as 15 minutes on a clock	*I know that a quarter turn makes a right angle.* *I can point out right angles in the classroom.*

Activity 1

Prior learning

Children know that £1 is equal to 100p. They can use a range of strategies to solve single-step and two-step money and measure problems. They can discuss ways of solving problems in a group.

Framework objective

Solve problems involving addition, subtraction, multiplication or division in contexts of numbers, measures or pounds and pence

Vocabulary

problem, solution, puzzle, pattern, method, sign, operation, symbol, number sentence, equation, mental calculation, written calculation, informal method, jottings, diagrams, pictures, images, coin, pound (£), pence, price, cost, pay, costs more/less, change, total, how much

Resources

Interactive activity: Money, money, money
Resource sheet: Self-assessment
Classroom resources: real or play coins

1 Money, money, money

Work with a group. Reveal the interactive activity 'Money, money, money'. Invite those children you particularly want to assess to identify each coin and drag it into the white area. Input £2.35 into the space and invite individual children to make that amount by dragging and dropping coins into the working area. Invite several different responses for each amount. Pose problems, such as: *Samantha has £5. She gives £1.99 to one friend and £1.50 to another. How much money does she have left?* Invite children to explain how they found the answer. Decide whether to use the self-assessment sheet for children to record their achievements and what they need to do next.

Teacher support

Less confident learners: Pose two-step problems with smaller amounts of money. For example: *Samantha had £1. She gave 25p to one friend and 35p to another. How much did she have left?*
More confident learners: Adapt the two-step problems you ask so that they involve amounts of money to £10.

Common misconception

Children do not use the least number of coins to make an amount.
Put a selection of coins on the table and write a target amount on the board, such as £3.86. Ask children to start with the pounds and to say what coins they would use to make £3. Discuss the coins that could be used to make 80p by placing 50p, 20p and 10p coins for children to consider. Encourage children to start with 50p, and then look at whether they can add one or more 20p coins. Repeat for 10p coins. Then look at ways to make 6p.

Probing questions

- I have five coins. Together they total £1.75. What coins could they be?
- What other coins could they be?
- I have £2 and spend £1.25. How much will I have left?

Next steps

Support: Pose two-step problems, using addition and/or subtraction. Remind the children of the problem-solving steps: read and identify the question, decide where to start, follow a plan, review and choose next move, solve, and check answers. Encourage the children to concentrate on one strategy (for example, partitioning for addition). See also Year 2 Block D Unit 2.
Extension: Give children two-step problems with a mix of operations. Ensure that they consider a variety of strategies. See also Year 3 Block D Unit 1.

Activity 2

Prior learning

Children can add or subtract multiples of 10. They can find the difference of one- and two-digit numbers and use doubling and halving. They can add or subtract pairs of two-digit numbers using a variety of strategies.

Framework objective

Add or subtract mentally a one-digit number or a multiple of ten to or from any two-digit number; use practical and informal written methods to add or subtract two-digit numbers

Vocabulary

add, plus, sum, total, subtract, take away, minus, difference, inverse

Resources

Resource sheets: Multiples of 10 cards, 100-square, 0–100 number lines, Self-assessment
Classroom resources: paper and pens

2 Totals and differences

Provide the 'Multiples of 10' cards for each child. Ask them to shuffle the cards, and then pick two. They find the total of the two numbers chosen and their difference. Encourage the children to consider such strategies as near doubles, partitioning, bridging 10, adding a near multiple of 10 and adjusting, counting on. They should record their work in their own way on plain paper. You could provide 100-squares and number lines if necessary. Observe those you wish to assess, noting the strategies they use and asking them to explain their methods. Decide whether to use the self-assessment sheet for children to record their achievements and what they need to do next.

Teacher support

Less confident learners: Give these children 0–30 number cards. Encourage them to use one particular strategy – for example, bridging 10 for addition, counting on for subtraction.
More confident learners: Ask the children to pick three number cards to total and to subtract each of the smaller numbers in turn from the largest.

Common misconception

Children have difficulty counting on from a smaller number, when crossing tens boundaries.
Demonstrate how to find the difference between two numbers that involve crossing one tens boundary, such as 45 - 38. Show how to find the smaller number on a number line, count up two places to the next tens boundary, and then five more to reach 45. Write 2 + 5 = 7, and complete the subtraction: 45 - 38 = 7.

Probing questions

- How could I subtract 24 from 38? Can you think of another way?
- Which strategy would be best for 26 + 25? Why?

Next steps

Support: Choose another strategy for children to learn so that they gradually build up a repertoire. For example, for bridging 10, encourage them to use a number line to help work out 37 + 8: count on 3 to 40, and then count on the remaining 5 to give the total 45; write the number sentence: 37 + 8 = 45. See also Year 2 Block D Unit 2.
Extension: Ask the children to explain partitioning, adding/subtracting a near multiple of 10 and adjusting, near doubles, bridging 10 and counting on. They should give a calculation to demonstrate each method. See also Year 3 Block A Unit 1.

Activity 3

Prior learning
Children can estimate, measure and compare lengths, weights and capacities. They can estimate length using 'just more/less than' or 'about'. They are beginning to estimate in hundreds of grams/kilograms and in hundreds of millilitres/litres.

Framework objective
Estimate, compare and measure lengths, weights and capacities, choosing and using standard units (m, cm, kg, litre) and suitable measuring instruments

Vocabulary
measuring scale, compare, measure, weigh, further, metre (m), centimetre (cm), tape measure, kilogram (kg), half-kilogram, gram (g), capacity, contains, litre (l), half-litre, millilitre (ml)

Resources
Interactive activity: Weight
Resource sheet: Self-assessment
Classroom resources: weighing scales

3 Weight

Work with a group. Reveal the interactive activity 'Weight'. Ask: *How many grams are the same as one kilogram?* Drag a 100g weight onto the scale pan. Target questions to those you wish to assess. *What weight is the pointer pointing to? What will happen if another 100g weight is added? What is the total weight now?* Repeat for nine 100g weights. *How many more 100g weights will make one kilogram?* Ask the children to write other combinations of weights to make one kilogram (for example, one 500g and five 100g weights). Decide whether to use the self-assessment sheet for children to record their achievements and what they need to do next.

Teacher support
Less confident learners: Give the children opportunities to drag and drop the weights, and describe how many are on the scales and state the total weight.
More confident learners: Ask the children to find all the possible ways to use 100g, 200g and 500g weights to make one kilogram, recording their methods.

Common misconception
Children cannot read the scale on a set of weighing scales.
Use real weighing scales. Place an item that weighs about one kilogram on them and ask children to point at the needle and tell you which whole kilogram it is closest to. Ask children to say whether a heavier item will make the needle point closer to 0 or closer to 5kg. Demonstrate what happens with an actual item. Repeat for a lighter item.

Probing questions
- Can you tell me two weights that together make one kilogram?
- Can you tell me any other combinations?
- What about half a kilogram?

Next steps
Support: Give the children the opportunity to use the interactive activity 'Weight' to practise reading scales by dragging weights onto the pan and totalling them. Give them goals to reach and encourage them to do this using the fewest weights. See also Year 2 Block D Unit 2.
Extension: Ask the children to draw their own scales and weights to show 1kg. They should use imaginary 50g, 100g, 200g and 500g weights, and find as many possibilities as they can. See also Year 3 Block D Unit 1.

Activity 4

Prior learning
Children can read a scale and measuring jug to the nearest division. They can use a ruler to measure to the nearest centimetre.

Framework objective
Read the numbered divisions on a scale, and interpret the divisions between them (e.g. on a scale from 0 to 25 with intervals of 1 shown but only the divisions 0, 5, 10, 15 and 20 numbered); use a ruler to draw and measure lines to the nearest centimetre

Vocabulary
measuring scale, compare, measure, weigh, further, metre (m), centimetre (cm), tape measure, kilogram (kg), half-kilogram, gram (g), capacity, contains, litre (l), half-litre, millilitre (ml)

Resources
Resource sheet: Self-assessment
Classroom resources: rulers, pencils, A4 paper

4 Draw the line

Ask the children to draw lines of different lengths (for example, 9cm, 24cm, 13cm, 16cm). Invite them to swap their papers with a partner and to measure each other's lines. Next, provide the children with opportunities to draw lines to the nearest centimetre according to different criteria (for example, closer to 20cm than 10cm, longer than 15cm, shorter than 21cm). Once they have completed this activity, decide whether to use the self-assessment sheet for children to record their achievements and what they need to do next.

Teacher support
Less confident learners: Ask these children to draw lines to the nearest 5cm (for example, 15cm, 10cm, 20cm).
More confident learners: Challenge the children to draw zigzag lines that have a given total length - for example, a zigzag in three parts that is 24cm long in total.

Common misconception
Children cannot estimate length.
Give children plenty of practical experience by encouraging them to draw lines 5cm, 10cm, 20cm and 30cm long. Ask them to find items in the classroom that are about these lengths.

Probing questions
- What do you need to remember when you are measuring with a ruler?
- If I drew a line to this mark, how long will it be?
- How long would this line be if it were 3cm longer?

Next steps
Support: Encourage the children to practise drawing lines to measurements that you give. Accept lines that are 2cm longer or shorter than the given lengths. See also Year 2 Block D Unit 2.
Extension: Ask the children to cut an A4 sheet of paper into strips of particular widths (for example, 5cm) and to measure the width of the strip that was left. Invite them to swap their strips with a partner to check. See also Year 3 Block D Unit 1.

Activity 5

Prior learning
Children recognise that the minute hand makes a quarter turn for a quarter of an hour. They know that an hour is 60 minutes and that by halving twice they get 15 minutes. They can read 'o'clock', 'half past', 'quarter to' and 'quarter past' times using the digital vocabulary.

Framework objective

Use units of time (seconds, minutes, hours, days) and know the relationships between them; read the time to the quarter-hour; identify time intervals, including those that cross the hour

Vocabulary

time, clock, watch, digital, analogue, hours (h), minutes (min), seconds (s), quarter to, quarter past

Resources

Interactive activity: Give me five!
Resource sheets: Self-assessment, Clock faces
Classroom resources: clocks with moveable hands (one per child)

5 Give me five!

Reveal the interactive activity 'Give me five!'. Show quarter to three and ask the children to show this on their clocks. *How would we show this on the digital clock?* Show five past ten on the analogue clock and 10:30 on the digital clock. Ask the children to show 10:30 on their clock faces, and to count in fives to find the time interval between the two times (25 minutes). Repeat for other time intervals. Decide whether to use the self-assessment sheet for children to record their achievements and what they need to do next.

Teacher support

Less confident learners: Ask the children to show o'clock, half- and quarter-past times on analogue clocks and to write them in digital format.
More confident learners: Ask the children to draw times that are five minutes apart on the resource sheet 'Clock faces', and to write the times in digital format.

Common misconception

Children cannot read and write digital times.
Look at the digital clock on the interactive activity 'Give me five!'. Use the pen tool to write 'Hours' and 'Minutes' above the appropriate parts of the clock. Click 'randomise' and invite children to say the hours and minutes shown, and what they might be doing at that time.

Probing questions

- How can you use a clock to help you work out how many minutes there are between 2:15 and 2:45?
- What would 4:30 look like on an analogue clock?
- If it is 20 minutes past 7, what time will it be in 10 minutes?

Next steps

Support: Give regular opportunities for the children to say o'clock, half-past, quarter-past and quarter-to times and show them on clock faces. As they find each one, ask them to write the time in digital format too. See also Year 2 Block D Unit 2.
Extension: Once the children are confident with o'clock, half-past, quarter-to and quarter-past on analogue and digital clocks, concentrate on times to the nearest five minutes. Ask them to show the times on a clock, then to work out and write the time in digital format. See also Year 3 Block D Unit 1.

Activity 6

Prior learning

Children can give instructions for position, direction and movement using whole, half and quarter turns. They recognise that a quarter turn produces a right angle and is the same as 15 minutes on a clock.

Framework objective

Recognise and use whole, half and quarter turns, both clockwise and anticlockwise; know that a right angle represents a quarter turn

Vocabulary

direction, route, clockwise, anticlockwise, quarter turn, right angle, straight line

Resources

Resource sheet: Self-assessment
Classroom resources: clocks with moveable hands (one per child), 2D shapes, geo-strips, squared paper, rulers

6 Right angles

Work with small groups whom you wish to observe. Ask the children to place the hands on their individual clocks at 12 o'clock, then to move the minute hand clockwise to quarter past 12. Ask them the size of turn they have made and what this resembles (a quarter turn and a right angle). Encourage them to identify right angles in the classroom (for example, corners of doors, cupboards and windows). Ask them to draw some in different orientations with rulers on squared paper. Provide 2D shapes and ask the children to sort them into shapes that have right angles and those that do not. Decide whether to use the self-assessment sheet for the children to record their achievements and what they need to do next.

Teacher support

Less confident learners: Show these children how to make a right-angle corner by folding a sheet of paper in half and half again. Ask them to use these to find right angles in the classroom.
More confident learners: Challenge these children to find examples of angles that are greater or less than a right angle.

Common misconception

Children cannot recognise right angles in the classroom.
Make the connection between right angles and square corners. Ask children to say how many right angles they can see on a sheet of paper, on their reading book, on a door, and on the ceiling.

Probing questions

- Which of these shapes has a right angle? Where is it?
- Can you see right angles in the classroom? Where are they?
- Can you see something that is less than/greater than a right angle?

Next steps

Support: Give the children geo-strips to make right angles. Alternatively, ask them to make a right-angle measurer by folding a piece of paper in half and half again. They should then check corners of objects around the classroom to see if they are right angles. See also Year 2 Block D Unit 2.
Extension: Provide the children with 2D shapes to sort onto a one-criterion Carroll diagram (has/doesn't have a right angle). See also Year 3 Block D Unit 2.

Units 1, 2 & 3 Periodic assessment

These activities can be used at the end of this block to assess those children that you think have achieved the objectives.

New numbers

Framework objective
Add or subtract mentally a single-digit number or a multiple of 10 to or from any two-digit number; use practical and informal written methods to add or subtract two-digit numbers

Learning outcomes
- I can add and subtract some numbers in my head.
- I can add and subtract bigger numbers using equipment or notes to help.

1. Provide 1-9 digit cards and some + and – instruction cards. Give the children a two-digit number (for example, 24) and ask them to pick a digit card and an instruction card and follow the instruction (such as + 6). They should record how they worked out their answer. They then take the answer as their next number to work with and pick another digit and instruction card.

2. Provide 10–50 number cards. The children pick pairs of cards and make an addition and a subtraction calculation using both cards. They should think of two strategies, using the second as a check. They should make written notes of the strategies they used. Ask them to complete three sets of calculations. If necessary, provide number lines, 100-squares and apparatus.

Time test

Framework objective
Use units of time (seconds, minutes, hours, days) and know the relationships between them; read the time to the quarter hour; identify time intervals, including those that cross the hour

Learning outcomes
- I can estimate how long an activity might take, then check using a timer.
- I can tell the time when it is something o'clock or half past the hour.
- I know that one hour is the same as 60 minutes.
- I can tell the time when it is quarter past, half past or quarter to the hour.
- I know that quarter past three is the same time as three fifteen.
- I know that there are 24 hours in a day.
- I can use a clock face to help me to count in steps of five minutes.

1. The children need individual clocks and the resource sheet 'Clocks'. Call out o'clock and half-past times for the children to show on their clocks. Check that they have positioned the hour hand correctly between the two hour numbers for half-past times. Once they have found several of each, set some problems in context. For example: *It is lunchtime at 12 o'clock. Recorder club starts half an hour later. Show me what time recorder club starts.* After the children have found the time, ask them to draw the hands on the first clock on resource sheet 'Clocks' and label it. Repeat for other problems.

2. The children will need individual clocks. Call out o'clock, half-past, quarter-to and quarter-past times for them to find on their clocks. Check that they have positioned the hour hand correctly and ask them to write the times digitally. Next, give the children the cards cut from the resource sheet 'Time test (1)' to match. Once they have matched them, they should stick the clocks onto paper as a record of what they have done.

3. Give the children individual clocks, and ask them to find a time (for example, half past seven). Ask them to count in steps of five minutes, and tell you how long it will be until it is eight o'clock. Provide each child with a copy of the worksheet 'Time test (2)' and ask them to find the time differences by counting in steps of five minutes.

BLOCK D

Clocks

12
1
2
3
4
5
6
7
8
9
10
11

12
1
2
3
4
5
6
7
8
9
10
11

12
1
2
3
4
5
6
7
8
9
10
11

12
1
2
3
4
5
6
7
8
9
10
11

12
1
2
3
4
5
6
7
8
9
10
11

12
1
2
3
4
5
6
7
8
9
10
11

Time test (1)

- Cut out the clocks.
- Pair the clocks that say the same time. Stick them onto paper.

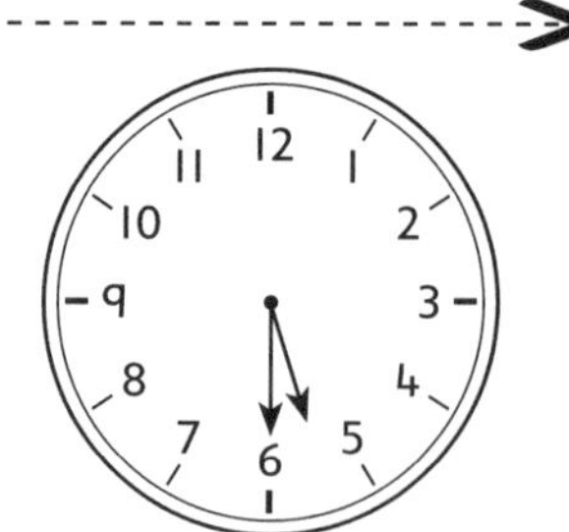

7 : 15

5 : 30

8 : 30

12 : 00

1 : 00

9 : 45

3 : 45

BLOCK E

Securing number facts, relationships and calculating

Expected prior learning

Check that children can already:

- solve problems involving doubling or halving, combining groups of 2, 5 or 10, or sharing into equal groups
- count on or back in ones, twos, fives and tens and use this knowledge to derive the multiples of 2, 5 and 10 to the tenth multiple
- recall the doubles of all numbers to at least 10
- use the vocabulary of halves and quarters in context.

Objectives overview

The text in this diagram identifies the focus of mathematics learning within the block.

Key aspects of learning

- Enquiry
- Problem solving
- Reasoning
- Information processing
- Motivation

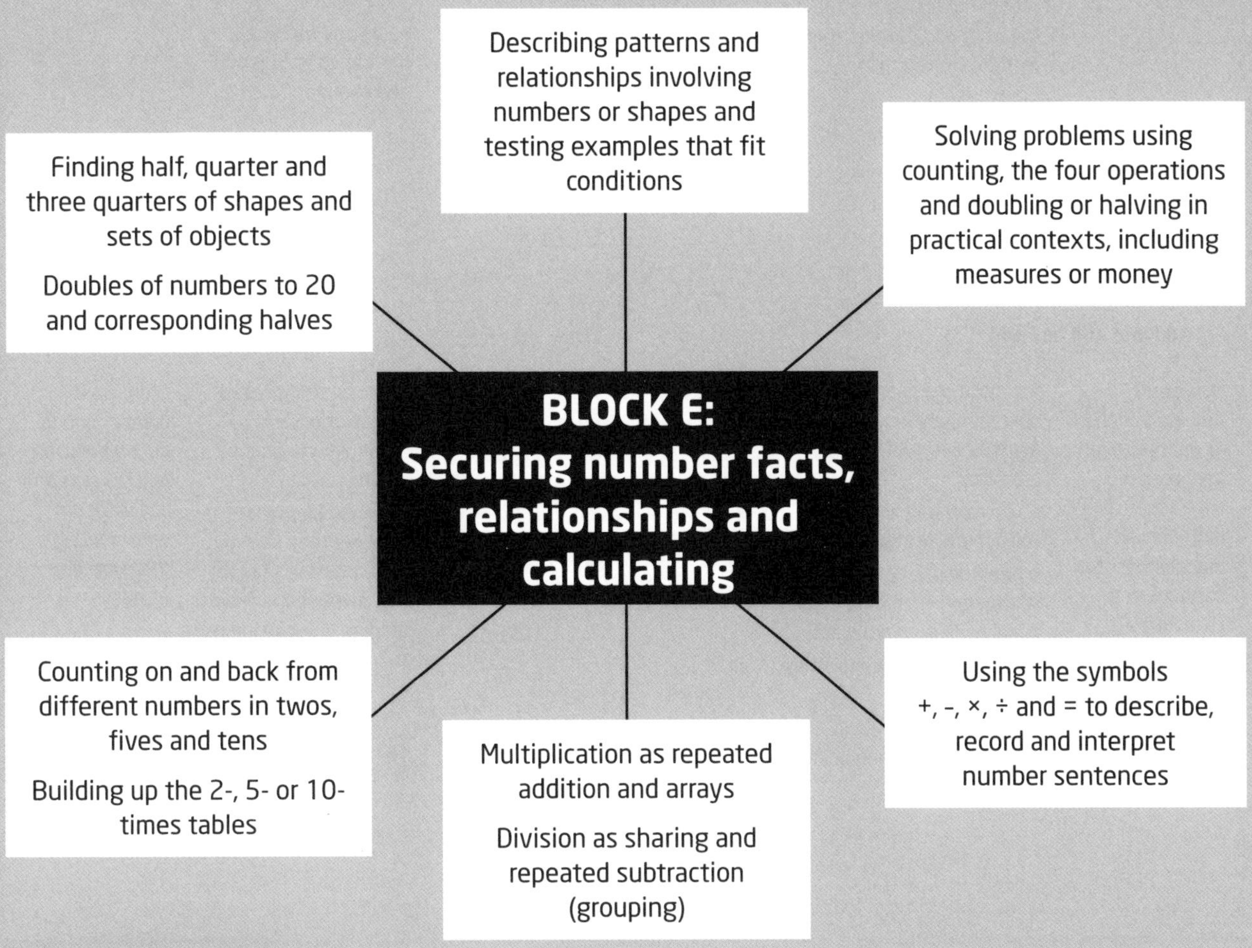

BLOCK E: Securing number facts, relationships and calculating

Describing patterns and relationships involving numbers or shapes and testing examples that fit conditions

Finding half, quarter and three quarters of shapes and sets of objects

Doubles of numbers to 20 and corresponding halves

Solving problems using counting, the four operations and doubling or halving in practical contexts, including measures or money

Counting on and back from different numbers in twos, fives and tens

Building up the 2-, 5- or 10-times tables

Multiplication as repeated addition and arrays

Division as sharing and repeated subtraction (grouping)

Using the symbols +, –, ×, ÷ and = to describe, record and interpret number sentences

Unit 1 Securing number facts, relationships and calculating

Introduction

In this unit, children extend their understanding of counting on and back in steps of 1, 2, 5 and 10 from different starting numbers. They record sequences, describe patterns, find missing numbers and predict others that would be in a sequence. They find missing numbers in number sentences involving addition and subtraction. They understand repeated addition as multiplication and use arrays and number lines to help them solve problems involving these skills. They learn that division is grouping as well as repeated subtraction. They find halves and quarters of groups of objects and numbers.

Framework objectives	Assessment focuses		Success criteria for Year 2	Learning outcomes
	Level 2	Level 1		
(1) Lots and lots				
Identify and record the information or calculation needed to solve a puzzle or problem; carry out the steps or calculations and check the solution in the context of the problem	• select the mathematics they use in some classroom activities, e.g. with support • make connections and apply their knowledge to similar situations • use mathematical content from levels 1 and 2 to solve problems and investigate • begin to represent their work using symbols and simple diagrams, e.g. with support • begin to appreciate the need to record and develop their own methods of recording	• use mathematics as an integral part of classroom activities, e.g. with support • engage with practical mathematical activities involving sorting, counting and measuring by direct comparison • begin to understand the relevance of mathematical ideas to everyday situations by using them in role-play • represent their work with objects or pictures	• can solve problems involving counting, adding or subtracting, doubling or halving • can use practical and informal written methods to find solutions • can solve problems that involve counting up to find the total of several coins of the same value • can pay for items costing up to 50p and find change	*I know what information I need to use to solve a problem and can describe what I did step by step.* *I can record it in a number sentence and check if my answer makes sense.*
(2) Add and add and add				
Represent repeated addition as multiplication, and repeated subtraction as division; use practical, written methods and vocabulary to support multiplication and division	• choose the appropriate operation when solving addition and subtraction problems • use repeated addition to solve multiplication problems • begin to use repeated subtraction or sharing equally to solve division problems • record their work in writing, e.g. • record their mental calculations as number sentences	• record their work, e.g. • record their work with objects, pictures or diagrams	• can count repeated groups of objects by counting in twos, five or tens • can explore what numbers they can land on by starting at zero on a number line then jumping along in jumps of 2, 5 or 10	*I can use a number line to do multiplication and division and can work out remainders if there are any.*

BLOCK E

Unit 1 Securing number facts, relationships and calculating

Framework objectives	Assessment focuses: Level 2	Assessment focuses: Level 1	Success criteria for Year 2	Learning outcomes
3 Which answer?				
Use the symbols +, -, ×, ÷ and = to record and interpret number sentences involving all four operations; calculate the value of an unknown in a number sentence	• record their work in writing, e.g. • record their mental calculations as number sentences	• record their work, e.g. • record their work with objects, pictures or diagrams • begin to use the symbols + and = to record additions	• can write number sentences for number puzzles and word problems	*I know how to write number sentences for multiplication and division as well as addition and subtraction.* *I can explain what my number sentence means.*
4 Dicey doubling				
Understand that halving is the inverse of doubling and derive and recall doubles of all numbers to 20, and the corresponding halves	• understand halving as a way of 'undoing' doubling and vice versa • use mental calculation strategies to solve number problems including those involving money and measures • begin to use halves and quarters, e.g. • work out halves of numbers up to 20 and begin to recall them	• begin to know some addition facts e.g. • doubles of numbers to double 5	• can solve problems involving doubling or halving in the context of numbers, measures or money	*I know doubles of numbers up to 10 and I can use what I know to work out halves.* *I understand the connection between doubling and halving.*
5 Multiple patterns				
Derive and recall multiplication facts for the 2-, 5- and 10-times tables and the related division facts; recognise multiples of 2, 5 and 10	• recognise sequences of numbers, including odd and even numbers • choose the appropriate operation when solving addition and subtraction problems • use repeated addition to solve multiplication problems • begin to use repeated subtraction or sharing equally to solve division problems	• order numbers to 10 • begin to count in twos	• can count in steps of 2, 5 and 10 • can record sequences and describe patterns in the numbers	*I can recognise some of the 2-, 5- and 10-times tables and can explain the patterns I see.* *I can use these patterns to see if other numbers belong to the sequence.*
6 Which fraction?				
Find one half, one quarter and three quarters of shapes and sets of objects	• begin to use halves and quarters • work out halves of numbers up to 20 and begin to recall them • relate the concept of half of a small quantity to the concept of half of a shape, e.g. • shade one half or one quarter of a given shape including those divided into equal regions	• begin to use the fraction one half, e.g. • halve shapes including folding paper shapes, lengths of string • put water in a clear container so that is it about 'half-full' • halve an even number of objects	• can divide small amounts into different-sized groups • can find halves of even numbers to 20	*I can use what I know about halving numbers to help me to work out half and a quarter of a set of objects or a shape.* *I can also work out three quarters.*

Activity 1

Prior learning
Children can solve problems involving counting, adding or subtracting, doubling or halving. They understand the value of all coins. They can pay for items costing up to 50p and find change.

Framework objective
Identify and record the information or calculation needed to solve a puzzle or problem; carry out the steps or calculations and check the solution in the context of the problem

Vocabulary
problem, solve, calculate, calculation, inverse, answer, method, explain, predict, pattern, order

Resources
Interactive activity: Lots and lots
Resource sheet: Self-assessment
Classroom resources: bag of potatoes, number lines and counters

1 Lots and lots

Work with a group. Reveal the interactive activity 'Lots and lots'. Show the bag of potatoes and say that these cost £2 per bag. Ask the children to show this amount in pound coins on the screen. *I want to buy four bags of potatoes. What would you do to find the total cost? Record your method. What is another way that you could show this? How can you check your answer?* Repeat for different numbers of bags of potatoes and prices. Decide whether to use the self-assessment sheet for children to record their achievements and what they need to do next.

Teacher support
Less confident learners: Work with the cost at £2 and the number of bags to 10.
More confident learners: Work with prices up to £5 and the number of bags to 10: *The cost of one bag is £4. If I buy seven bags, how much will that be?*

Common misconception
Children do not recognise which operation to use to solve a puzzle or problem.
Pose a problem, such as: *Chocolates cost 6p each. How much will five chocolates cost?* Ask children to role-play the situation to help them understand it. Encourage them to draw pictures of the chocolates and label each chocolate with a 6p price tag. *What number sentence could you write for the calculation?* (6p + 6p + 6p + 6p + 6p = 30p or 5 × 6 = 30.) Discuss that children could use either repeated addition or multiplication. Repeat for other problems.

Probing questions
- What do you think this problem is asking you to do?
- How could you work out the cost of five apples if each apple costs 8p?
- Can you think of two different ways to record this?

Next steps
Support: Work on repeated addition, using a number line as well as practical apparatus. Set up arrays of items (for example, two rows of six counters) and ask the children to draw loops in twos along the number line to make 12. Write the multiplication sentence to match this and explain. See also Year 1 Block E Unit 3.
Extension: Pose problems. Expect the children to work out the problems using partitioning and multiplication, and check their answer with repeated addition. See also Year 2 Block E Unit 2.

BLOCK E

Activity 2

Prior learning
Children can count in twos, fives or tens. They can use practical and written methods to support addition or subtraction of a one-digit number or a multiple of 10 to or from a one-digit or two-digit number.

Framework objective
Represent repeated addition and arrays as multiplication, and sharing and repeated subtraction (grouping) as division; use practical and informal written methods and related vocabulary to support multiplication and division, including calculations with remainders

Vocabulary
count on, count back, lots of, groups of, equal groups of, grouping, array, row, column, multiply, multiplication, multiplied by (×), multiple, share equally, divide, division, divided by (÷), remainder, round up, round down, double, halve

Resources
Interactive activity: Add and add and add
Resource sheet: Self-assessment
Classroom resources: counters, 0–100 number line

2 Add and add and add

Display the interactive activity 'Add and add and add' and show a 0–100 number line. Write a calculation such as 5 × 8 on the screen. Invite a child to draw jumps along the number line to show this multiplication and to describe what they have done. Ask someone else to check by jumping back in the same way and to explain what they did and why. Encourage the link with grouping. Repeat for other calculations. Focus on division, asking the children to group 25 into groups of 5 (and so on). Decide whether to use the self-assessment sheet for children to record their achievements and what they need to do next.

Teacher support
Less confident learners: Focus on multiplying, using the number line.
More confident learners: Focus on division with remainders, asking the children to check by multiplying and then adding the remainder.

Common misconceptions
Children do not understand that repeated addition and multiplication give the same result.
Provide counters and ask children to group ten of them in twos. Explain that 2 + 2 + 2 + 2 + 2 = 10, which is the same as five lots of two. Count in twos five times, using fingers to show 5 × 2 gives the same result.

Children do not understand that repeated subtraction and division give the same result.
Give children ten counters and ask them to take groups of two counters away. Write 10 - 2 - 2 - 2 - 2 - 2 = 0. *How many groups of two have we subtracted?* Explain that this can also be written as 10 ÷ 2 = 5.

Probing questions
- What do these jumps on the number line show?
- How could you record this?
- There are ten pencils in three boxes and four more pencils. How many pencils are there altogether?

Next steps
Support: Give plenty of opportunities for children to practise jumping in steps of 2, 5 and 10 along a number line. See also Year 1 Block E Unit 3.
Extension: Encourage the children to make up their own problems that involve division with remainders. See also Year 2 Block E Unit 2.

BLOCK E

Activity 3

Prior learning

Children solve practical problems involving repeated groups either by adding or taking away. They can describe and explain problems using practical materials, diagrams or numbers. They can solve problems involving sharing'.

Framework objective

Use the symbols +, -, ×, ÷ and = to record and interpret number sentences involving all four operations; calculate the value of an unknown in a number sentence (e.g. □ ÷ 2 = 6, 30 - □ = 24)

Vocabulary

count on, count back, lots of, groups of, equal groups of, grouping, array, row, column, multiply, multiplication, multiplied by (×), multiple, share equally, divide, division, divided by (÷), remainder, round up, round down, double, halve

Resources

Resource sheet: Self-assessment
Classroom resources: counting objects, number lines, whiteboards and pens

3 Which answer?

Work with a small group of children. Pose four problems that involve multiplication or division. For example:

- There are 20 wheels. How many cars?
- I had eight conkers. Ben had twice as many. How many did Ben have?
- How many fives make 35?
- Reiza planted three tomato plants. Each plant had ten tomatoes. How many tomatoes were there?

For each problem, ask the children to write a number sentence on their whiteboards. When all the children have an answer, ask them to show their calculations and discuss their methods. Decide whether to use the self-assessment sheet for children to record their achievements and next steps.

Teacher support

Less confident learners: Give these children numbers to 20 to group in twos, fives and tens practically, and have them check their answers by jumping back from the starting number on a number line.
More confident learners: Ask these children to make up their own problems involving multiplying or dividing by 3 or 4.

Common misconception

Children do not recognise when to use multiplication or division.
Pose a variety of word problems that involve multiplication or division. For example: *Sally's book is 10cm wide. Josh's book is twice as wide. How wide is Josh's book?* Discuss how children decide what operation to use. Stress that whenever more than one of something is needed, then the operation is multiplication. If you need one of something, then division is needed.

Probing questions

- How many tens are there in 60?
- I can see 12 legs. How many ducks are there?
- Which numbers could I put in this number sentence to make it true? □ ÷ 2 = □

Next steps

Support: Provide opportunities for the children to continue to use practical equipment to multiply and divide and then to translate this to jumps forward or back along a number line. See also Year 1 Block E Unit 2.
Extension: Provide opportunities for the children to begin to multiply and divide numbers to 100 by 2, 3, 4, 5, and 10. See also Year 2 Block E Unit 2.

Activity 4

Prior learning

Children can derive and recall doubles of all number to ten, and the corresponding halves.

Framework objective

Understand that halving is the inverse of doubling and derive and recall doubles of all numbers to 20, and the corresponding halves

Vocabulary

add, multiply, inverse, halve, halved, double, doubled

Resources

Worksheet: Dicey doubling
Classroom resources: dice, models to illustrate a half (for example, a biscuit, plastic farm animals, coins, counters)

4 Dicey doubling

Give each pair of children two dice and a copy of the worksheet 'Dicey doubling'. They then take it in turns to throw the two dice, total the numbers rolled and double the answer, recording what they do as number sentences. Ask them to do this ten times each. They then total their scores to find who is the winner. Sit with pairs of children you wish to assess.

Teacher support

Less confident learners: Ask these children to throw one dice and then double the number rolled.
More confident learners: Ask these children to add an extra rule: if they get an even total, they halve their answer; if their total is odd, they double it.

Common misconceptions

Children have little concept of what 'half' means.
Provide concrete models to illustrate 'half'. Ask children to break a biscuit in half. Provide plastic farm animals and say: *A farmer has six horses and puts half of them in the field. How many horses should go into the field?* Focus on two halves being two equal amounts. Repeat for other examples of halving.

Children are not confident at linking halves and doubles.
Use the inversion loop model with numbers of counters to illustrate:

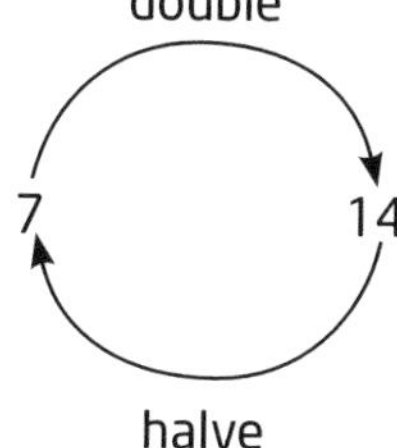

Probing questions

- How would you describe how to double and halve?
- I am thinking of a number. I double it and get 18. What number was it?
- Two identical books cost £14. How much is one book?

Next steps

Support: Focus on doubles of numbers to 10, and the corresponding halves. Use practical apparatus such as money to help children link the two operations. Pose real-life problems. See also Year 2 Block B Unit 1.
Extension: Focus on halving numbers to 50, and the corresponding halves. Pose questions, such as: *I'm thinking of a number. Half my number is 24. What number am I thinking of?* See also Year 2 Block E Unit 2.

Activity 5

Prior learning
Children can count in steps of 2, 5 and 10. They can record sequences and describe patterns in the numbers.

Framework objective
Derive and recall multiplication facts for the 2-, 5- and 10-times tables and the related division facts; recognise multiples of 2, 5 and 10

Vocabulary
multiply, multiplication, multiplied by (×), multiple, share equally, divide, division, divided by (÷)

Resources
Interactive activity: Multiple patterns
Resource sheets: Match the cards, Self-assessment

5 Multiple patterns

Reveal the interactive activity 'Multiple patterns'. Ask the particular children you wish to assess to highlight the multiples of 5. For each multiple of 5, ask everyone to write the corresponding times-tables fact (for example, if you highlight 30, the children should write 5 × 6 = 30). Ask them what they notice about the multiples. (They all end with 0 or 5.) Ask the children to write the next three multiples of 5 after 50 (55, 60, 65). Repeat for multiples of 2 and 10. Decide whether to use the self-assessment sheet for children to record their achievements and what they need to do next.

Teacher support
Less confident learners: Concentrate on multiples of 10.
More confident learners: Ask the children to use a multiplication table to find common multiples of 2, 5 and 10 to 100 and to make a rule for these numbers, (for example, the numbers all end in zero).

Common misconception
Children do not link counting in equal steps to the operation of multiplication.
Use the resource sheet 'Match the cards'. Cut out the cards showing dots and repeated addition and multiplication sentences. Ask children to match them. For example:

5 + 5 + 5

5 × 3

Probing questions
- What number larger than 100 would be in the 5-times table? How can you prove that?
- Can you think of a number that is a multiple of 5 but not a multiple of 2 or 10?

Next steps
Support: Link counting in steps of 2, 5 and 10 to making jumps along a number line. Link to repeated addition and then the times-tables facts. See also Year 1 Block E Unit 3.
Extension: Extend to 3- and 4-times table multiplication and division facts. See also Year 2 Block B Unit 2.

Activity 6

Prior learning
Children can divide small amounts into different-sized groups. They can find halves of even numbers to 20.

Framework objective
Find one half, one quarter and three quarters of shapes and sets of objects

Vocabulary
fraction, part, equal parts, one whole, parts of a whole, number of parts, half, left over, fraction, one half, one quarter, three quarters

Resources
Interactive activity: Which fraction?
Resource sheet: Self-assessment
Classroom resources: coins, counters, strips of paper

6 Which fraction?

Reveal the interactive activity 'Which fraction?'. Drag six pennies onto the working area. Ask the children you wish to assess to drag half of them to one side. Next, put eight pennies on the working area. Ask the children to find a quarter of 8. Say: *Explain your answer and method.* Repeat with different numbers of pennies. Drag three pennies onto the board. *This is half of the money I have in my pocket. How much do I have in total? How do you know?* Repeat for one quarter. Decide whether to use the self-assessment sheet for children to record their achievements and what they need to do next.

Teacher support
Less confident learners: Focus on finding half of given numbers of coins.
More confident learners: Ask the children to find a half and a quarter of given amounts by identifying the number of 2p or 10p coins. For example: *Find half of 12p as six 2p coins.*

Common misconception
Children do not understand the relationship between a half and a quarter.
Give each child a strip of paper and ask them to fold it in half, and then open it to see two parts. Ask them to fold it in half again, and then in half again. They open it up to find four parts. Ask them to identify how many quarters are in one half. They should be able to see that there are two quarters in each half and that half of a half is a quarter.

Probing questions
- How can you find half of these ten counters?
- What about a quarter of these 12 counters?
- What can you tell me about the size of a quarter and a half?

Next steps
Support: To reinforce and consolidate, continue to give the children practical activities to work on (for example, making halves and quarters of piles of coins). See also Year 1 Block E Unit 3.
Extension: Provide opportunities for the children to explore eighths practically by folding strips of paper and halving piles of coins three times. See also Year 2 Block E Unit 2.

BLOCK E

Unit 2 Securing number facts, relationships and calculating

Introduction

The children know doubles of numbers to 10 and the related halves and can find doubles of numbers to 20 using partitioning. They recognise and write the fraction notation for ½ and ¼. They find half of a set of objects, and recognise that finding half of a number is the same as dividing it by 2. They find a quarter of a set of objects by sharing them equally between 4 and use the appropriate vocabulary related to halves and quarters. They establish multiplication and division facts for the 2-, 5- and 10-times tables by counting in twos, fives and tens. If necessary, they use practical apparatus, counting or drawing to support them. They relate division to multiplication and use their knowledge of multiplication and division facts to answer simple word problems. They record calculations using the appropriate symbols. Threaded throughout the block are elements of the 'using and applying' objectives.

Framework objectives	Assessment focuses		Success criteria for Year 2	Learning outcomes
	Level 2	Level 1		
1 The answer is...				
Identify and record the information or calculation needed to solve a puzzle or problem; carry out the steps or calculations and check the solution in the context of the problem	• select the mathematics they use in some classroom activities, e.g. with support • find a starting point, identifying key facts/relevant information • use apparatus, diagrams, role-play etc to represent and clarify a problem • begin to represent their work using symbols and simple diagrams, e.g. with support • use pictures, diagrams and symbols to communicate their thinking, or demonstrate a solution or process	• use mathematics as an integral part of classroom activities, e.g. with support • engage with practical mathematical activities involving sorting, counting and measuring by direct comparison • begin to understand the relevance of mathematical ideas to everyday situations by using them in role-play • represent their work with objects or pictures	• can identify the information needed to solve problems • can use counting, practical equipment, diagrams or a number line to support, record or explain their answers	*I know what I need to do to help me solve a problem and then I can work out the answer.* *I can show how I solved a problem or puzzle and explain steps in my working.*
2 Lots of money				
Solve problems involving addition, subtraction, multiplication or division in contexts of numbers, measures or pounds and pence	• select the mathematics they use in some classroom activities, e.g. with support • move between different representations of a problem, e.g. a situation described in words, a diagram etc • use mathematical content from levels 1 and 2 to solve problems and investigate • choose the appropriate operation when solving addition and subtraction problems • begin to use repeated subtraction or sharing equally to solve division problems • solve number problems involving money and measures	• use mathematics as an integral part of classroom activities, e.g. with support • begin to understand the relevance of mathematical ideas to everyday situations by using them in role-play • solve addition/subtraction problems involving up to ten objects, e.g. • given a number work out 'how many more to make...' • choose which of given pairs of numbers add to a given total • solve measuring problems such as 'how many balance with...' • solve problems involving 1p or £1 coins	• can solve problems involving all four operations using counting, practical equipment, diagrams or a number line to support, record or explain their answers	*I can use calculations to solve problems and I know which calculation to use.*

Unit 2 Securing number facts, relationships and calculating

Framework objectives	Assessment focuses Level 2	Level 1	Success criteria for Year 2	Learning outcomes
③ Share with me				
Represent repeated addition and arrays as multiplication, and sharing and repeated subtraction as division; use practical and informal written methods and related vocabulary as support	• choose the appropriate operation when solving addition and subtraction problems • use repeated addition to solve multiplication problems • begin to use repeated subtraction or sharing equally to solve division problems • record their work in writing, e.g. • record their mental calculations as number sentences	• record their work, e.g. • record their work with objects, pictures or diagrams	• can understand that multiplication is repeated addition and that it can be represented using the multiplication symbol • can use a number line to support this, explaining what they do • can make the link to repeated subtraction	*I can use sharing to work out divisions and can explain what I did.*
④ Missing numbers				
Use the symbols +, −, ×, ÷ and = to record and interpret number sentences involving all four operations; calculate the value of an unknown in a number sentence	• understand halving as a way of 'undoing' doubling and vice versa • record their work in writing, e.g. • record their mental calculations as number sentences	• record their work, e.g. • record their work with objects, pictures or diagrams • begin to use the symbols + and = to record additions	• can record sequences, describe patterns and find missing numbers • can write number sentences to record addition, subtraction, multiplication and division calculations making use of the correct symbols	*I know how to write number sentences for multiplication and for division.* *I can explain what different numbers sentences mean.*
⑤ I just know it!				
Understand that halving is the inverse of doubling and derive and recall doubles of all numbers to 20, and the corresponding halves	• understand halving as a way of 'undoing' doubling and vice versa • use mental calculation strategies to solve number problems including those involving money and measures, e.g. • recall doubles to 10 + 10 and other significant doubles, e.g. double 50p is 100p or £1 • use knowledge of doubles to 10 + 10 to derive corresponding halves • begin to use halves and quarters, e.g. • work out halves of numbers up to 20 and begin to recall them	• begin to know some addition facts, e.g. • doubles of numbers to double 5	• can find doubles of numbers to 10 using practical resources or drawing • can record these using repeated addition and multiplication • can understand halving as the inverse operation to doubling • can find the halves of the doubles of numbers to 10	*I know some of my doubles up to 20.* *I can work out the rest and some others too.*

BLOCK E

Unit 2 Securing number facts, relationships and calculating

Framework objectives	Assessment focuses		Success criteria for Year 2	Learning outcomes
	Level 2	Level 1		
6 The fact is...				
Derive and recall multiplication facts for the 2-, 5- and10-times tables and the related division facts; recognise multiples of 2, 5 and 10	• recognise sequences of numbers, including odd and even numbers, e.g. • continue a sequence that increases or decreases in regular steps • recognise numbers from counting in tens or twos • choose the appropriate operation when solving addition and subtraction problems • use repeated addition to solve multiplication problems • begin to use repeated sbtraction or sharing equally to solve division problems	• order numbers to 10 • begin to count in twos	• can count in steps of 2, 5 and 10 • can remember some times-tables facts for the 2-, 5- and 10-times tables	*I know some of my times tables for 2, 5 and 10 and I can use counting or other strategies for those I don't know.* *I know that multiples of 5 end in 5 or zero.*
7 Which fraction?				
Find one half, one quarter and three quarters of shapes and sets of objects	• begin to use halves and quarters, e.g. • use the concept of a fraction of a small quantity in a practical context, such as sharing sweets between two and getting half each, among four and getting a quarter each • work out halves of numbers up to 20 and begin to recall them • relate the concept of half of a small quantity to the concept of half of a shape, e.g. • shade one half or one quarter of a given shape including those divided into equal regions	• begin to use the fraction one half, e.g. • halve shapes, including folding paper shapes, lengths of string • put water in a clear container so that it is about 'half full' • halve an even number of objects	• can find halves and quarters of shapes by folding • can find halves and quarters of a group of objects and numbers • can sort numbers into those that can be halved exactly and those that can't	*I can find half or a quarter of a set of objects.* *I can fold a piece of paper into halves or quarters.*

BLOCK E

Activity 1

Prior learning
Children can identify the information needed to solve problems. They can use counting, practical equipment, diagrams or a number line to support, record or explain their answers.

Framework objective
Identify and record the information or calculation needed to solve a puzzle or problem; carry out the steps or calculations and check the solution in the context of the problem

Vocabulary
problem, solve, calculate, calculation, inverse, answer, method, explain, predict, pattern, order

Resources
Resource sheets: Self-assessment, 0-30 number lines, 100-square, Multiplication square
Classroom resources: counters, 1p, 2p, 5p and 10p coins

1 The answer is...

Work with a group. Write the number 12 on the board. Ask the children to write different number sentences that have 12 as the answer. Encourage them to give examples of addition, subtraction, multiplication and division sentences. Give an example of each. For example: 10 + 2 = 12, 20 - 8 = 12, 2 × 6 = 12, 24 ÷ 2 = 12. Watch what children do, challenging them as appropriate. Next, give them another number up to 30 and ask them to do the exercise again without any help from you. Assess their ability to use all the operations and also to explain what they did. Decide whether to use the self-assessment sheet for children to record their achievements and what they need to do next.

Teacher support
Less confident learners: Ask the children to find ways to make numbers to 20. Give them number lines, the first few lines of 100-squares and multiplication tables to help them.
More confident learners: Challenge these children to find ways to make numbers between 30 and 50.

Common misconception
Children do not have strategies to find ways of making numbers.
Give children ten counters and ask them to find number pairs that total 10 by splitting the group in different ways (for example, 8 + 2, 4 + 6, 5 + 5). Put out different numbers of counters between 10 and 20, and ask children to work out what to take away to leave ten counters.

Probing questions
- If I want to make 15, what could I do?
- Are there any other ways?
- What helped you to find the answer?

Next steps
Support: Give the children ten coins each and ask them to use them to make additions that total 10p (such as 5p + 3p + 2p), recording their results as number sentences. Ask them to add groups of the same number of pennies to give 10p and link this to multiplication. See also Year 2 Block E Unit 1.
Extension: Ask the children to write multiplication sentences with the answer 24, and to write the corresponding division sentences as a check. See also Year 2 Block E Unit 3.

Activity 2

Prior learning
Children can solve problems involving all four operations using counting, practical equipment, diagrams or a number line to support, record or explain their answers.

Framework objective
Solve problems involving addition, subtraction, multiplication or division in contexts of numbers, measures or pounds and pence

Vocabulary
problem, solve, calculate, calculation, inverse, answer, method, explain, predict, pattern, order

Resources
Resource sheet: Self-assessment
Classroom resources: 2p, 5p and 10p coins

2 Lots of money

Work with a small group. Give the children three 10p coins and ask them to tell you how much money there is in total. Observe how they do this: do they add 10p three times or are they confident with multiplication and know 10 × 3 = 30? Encourage them to record their thinking in their own way. Repeat with four 5p coins and six 2p coins. Pose problems, such as: *I want to buy a magazine. It costs 90p. I have six 10p coins and four 5p coins. Do I have enough money?* Decide whether to use the self-assessment sheet for children to record their achievements and what they need to do next.

Teacher support
Less confident learners: Concentrate on amounts using 10p coins, moving to 5p coins and smaller when the children are confident.
More confident learners: Work with mixed amounts of money as answers to multiplication and additions. For example: two 5p coins, eight 2p coins and four 10p coins gives 10p + 16p + 40p = 66p.

Common misconceptions
Children have difficulty knowing the value of coins.
Give children 36 pennies and ask them to count them out into groups of ten, then exchange them for a 20p coin, a 10p coin, a 5p coin and a 1p coin. Ask the children to draw around the coins of the same type and write their values on the drawing, recording what they have done as a number sentence: 20p + 10p + 5p + 1p = 36p.

Children think that the bigger the coin, the greater its value.
Give children one each of 1p, 2p, 5p, 10p coins and ask them to order them according to size. Place the equivalent number of pennies under each and ask them to tell you which is worth the most/least.

Probing questions
- I used five 5p coins to buy a stamp. How much did the stamp cost?
- I spent 40p. What coins could I have used if they were all the same?

Next steps
Support: Ask the children to find totals of several 10p coins and to record the repeated addition, saying it aloud as they do so, and then write the multiplication. Repeat for 5p coins, then 2p coins. See also Year 2 Block B Unit 2.
Extension: Pose some problems. For example: *Paminda had four 10p coins, five 5p coins and three 2p coins. Fiona had six 10p coins and seven 2p coins. Who had the most money? What number sentences did you use to solve the problem?* See also Year 2 Block B Unit 3.

Activity 3

Prior learning

Children understand that multiplication is equivalent to repeated addition. They can use a number line to support this. They have experienced division as grouping and can make the link to repeated subtraction.

Framework objective

Represent repeated addition and arrays as multiplication, and sharing and repeated subtraction (grouping) as division; use practical and informal written methods and related vocabulary to support multiplication and division, including calculations with remainders

Vocabulary

count on, count back, lots of, groups of, equal groups of, grouping, array, row, column, multiply, multiplication, multiplied by (×), multiple, share equally, divide, division, divided by (÷), remainder, round up, round down, double, halve

Resources

Interactive activity: Share with me
Resource sheet: Self-assessment
Classroom resources: 1p coins, counters

3 Share with me

Display the interactive activity 'Share with me'. Drag 20 pennies onto the working area. *How many groups of equal size could you make with these pennies?* Provide pennies for each pair. Ask the children to investigate the different groups they can make, and to write corresponding number sentences. Encourage them to make as many different arrangements as they can (10 ÷ 2 = 5, 10 ÷ 5 = 2, 10 ÷ 1 = 10, 10 ÷ 1 = 10). Repeat for 30 pennies and then 15. Decide whether to use the self-assessment sheet for children to record their achievements and what they need to do next.

Teacher support

Less confident learners: Concentrate on sharing even number amounts practically into two groups.
More confident learners: Give these children amounts such that, when they are shared into groups of 2, 5 or 10, there will be a remainder.

Common misconception

Children do not understand the relationship between sharing and grouping.
Show children both aspects of division at the same time. Ask them to share a pile of 12 counters among four children. *How many counters does each have? Write the number sentence.* (12 ÷ 4 = 3) Ask children to group the counters so that there are four in each group. *How many counters are in each group? Write this as a number sentence.* (12 ÷ 4 = 3) Discuss how the number sentences are the same for both the sharing and the grouping. Repeat with 15 counters.

Probing questions

- What is the difference between sharing and grouping?
- Can I share 15 counters equally into two piles? Why not?
- Can I share 30 counters equally into ten piles? How do you know?

Next steps

Support: Practise sharing small numbers of objects between 2, 5 or 10 and also grouping objects into groups of 2, 5 or 10. See also Year 2 Block E Unit 1.
Extension: Encourage the children to look for a pattern when sharing into 2, 5 or 10 with remainders. For example: odd numbers will always have a remainder of 1 when shared between 2, a number one more than a multiple of 5 will always have a remainder of 1, a number two more will have a remainder of 2 (and so on). See also Year 2 Block E Unit 3.

Activity 4

Prior learning
Children record sequences, describe patterns and find missing numbers. They can write number sentences to record addition, subtraction, multiplication and division calculations.

Framework objective
Use the symbols +, -, ×, ÷ and = to record and interpret number sentences involving all four operations; calculate the value of an unknown in a number sentence (e.g. □ ÷ 2 = 6, 30 - □ = 24)

Vocabulary
place value, partition, ones, tens, hundreds, single-digit number, two-digit number, add, subtract, plus (+), minus (-), sign, equals (=), operation, symbol, number sentence, number line

Resources
Display page: Missing numbers
Resource sheet: Self-assessment
Classroom resources: counting objects, plastic cubes, counters

4 Missing numbers

Work with a group and provide counting objects. Reveal the display page 'Missing numbers' which shows some multiplication and division calculations with missing numbers. Ask the children what the first number sentence says and how they might find the missing number: 18 ÷ □ = 6. The children know they have 18 things and that they have to group them into six groups. They can use the practical apparatus to help demonstrate their explanation and find the answer. They can then make up a word problem to go with the number sentence. Decide whether to use the self-assessment sheet for children to record their achievements and what they need to do next.

Teacher support
Less confident learners: Give the children missing number sentences to 20 with the first number always present.
More confident learners: Give these children missing number sentences with numbers up to 100.

Common misconception
Children cannot use inverse operations to solve missing number problems.
Remind children that division 'undoes' multiplication and vice versa. For example, write 40 ÷ □ = 8. Put out 40 cubes. Explain that the problem is asking how many groups of 8 make 40. Children make groups of eight cubes, then count the groups. Write the number sentence: 40 ÷ 5 = 8. *What multiplication do we know that uses these numbers?* (5 × 8 = 40.) Explain how children can read the problem as 'How many eights make 40?' and use their knowledge of times-table facts to help them. Repeat for other multiplication/division facts.

Probing questions
- My number is 4. I do something to it and get 32. What did I do?
- Look at this number sentence: □ × 4 = 28. Can you find the missing number?
- Write a number sentence for this word problem: *I have 20 cakes. I put them onto four plates. There are five cakes on each plate.*

Next steps
Support: Work through some calculations such as 2 × 6 = 12, asking the children to show this practically with counters. Once they have done this, write the calculation as a missing number sentence and ask them to complete it. See also Year 2 Block A Unit 2.
Extension: Challenge the children to make up some missing-number problems for a friend to solve. See also Year 2 Block E Unit 3.

Activity 5

Prior learning
Children can find doubles of numbers to 10. They can record these using repeated addition and multiplication. They can find the halves of the doubles of numbers to 10.

Framework objective
Understand that halving is the inverse of doubling and derive and recall doubles of all numbers to 20, and the corresponding halves

Vocabulary
doubling, halving, double, halve

Resources
Display page: I just know it!
Resource sheet: Self-assessment
Classroom resources: whiteboards and pens, red and blue cubes

5 I just know it!

Work with a group you wish to assess. Reveal the display page 'I just know it!'. Ask the children to write 'double 6' as an addition number sentence on their whiteboards, then as a multiplication number sentence, and finally to write the answer and hold up their boards to show you when they're ready. Assess whether they know the answer or if they have to work it out. Repeat for 'double 12'. After the children have finished, ask how knowing double 10 might help. Repeat for 'double 15', then for 'double 17'. Ask: *Did knowing that double 15 is 30 help?* Decide whether to use the self-assessment sheet for children to record their achievements and what they need to do next.

Teacher support
Less confident learners: Work with doubles of numbers to 10 and multiples of 10 to 100.
More confident learners: Invite these children to find the doubles of numbers between 15 and 30.

Common misconception
Children find it difficult to derive doubles.
Ask children to write down all the doubles that they know (such as double 5 is 10, double 10 is 20). Take one of the doubles that they have written (for example, double 2 is 4), and put out two lots of two red cubes. Add a blue cube to each row and say: *Now we're going to double 3. We know that double 2 is 4. We've added two blue cubes to show double 3, so double 3 is double 2 add 2.* Repeat for other doubles, each time asking children to tell you how to work out the answer.

Probing questions
- Which doubles do you know?
- I think of a number and double it. I get 18. What number did I start with?
- I halved a number and got 14. What was my number?

Next steps
Support: Concentrate on doubles of numbers from 10 to 20, and the corresponding halves. Make up inversion loops by partitioning and doubling 10, then the units/ones, then recombining, using practical equipment if necessary. See also Year 1 Block E Unit 2.
Extension: Give the children 'near doubles' addition problems, such as: 16 + 17, 24 + 25. Ask them to record their method. For example: 16 + 17 = 16 + 16 + 1, 24 + 25 = 25 + 25 - 1. See also Year 2 Block B Unit 3.

Activity 6

Prior learning

Children can count in steps of 2, 5 and 10. They can remember some of the facts for the 2-, 5- and 10-times tables.

Framework objective

Derive and recall multiplication facts for the 2-, 5- and 10-times tables and the related division facts; recognise multiples of 2, 5 and 10

Vocabulary

multiply, multiplication, multiplied by (×), multiple, share equally, divide, division, divided by (÷)

Resources

Interactive activity: The fact is...
Resource sheet: Self-assessment
Classroom resources: whiteboards and pens, dice (including dice with the sixes replaced by threes)

6 The fact is...

Work with a group whom you wish to assess. Reveal the interactive activity 'The fact is...'. Highlight a multiple of 2, 5 or 10. Ask the children to write down the multiplication and division facts that they know that use that number. For example, for 12 they could write 2 × 6 = 12, 6 × 2 = 12, 12 ÷ 2 = 6 and 12 ÷ 6 = 2. (Make a note of any children who come up with others, such as 3 × 4 = 12.) Ask the children to hold up their whiteboards when they're ready. Repeat the exercise for other numbers. Decide whether to use the self-assessment sheet for children to record their achievements and next steps.

Teacher support

Less confident learners: Encourage the children to count in tens, using their fingers to keep track of the count. *Stop! How many lots of 10 make the number you're on?*
More confident learners: These children could move on to the 3-times table, linking it to counting in steps of 3.

Common misconception

Children cannot give tables facts 'out of order'.
Provide opportunities for children to give answers to tables facts at speed: Play Snap, where one player puts down 'question' cards (for example, 2 × 3, 2 × 6) and the other player puts down the 'answers' (6, 12). Play with the 1-times table first and when children become more confident include several tables. Children throw one dice and multiply their score by 2, 5 or 10. Start with the 1-times table and one dice, then two dice (with the sixes replaced by three), and finally two regular dice and a mix of times tables.

Probing questions

- How can you use 10 × 7 = 70 to work out 5 × 7 = 35?
- I had a number and multiplied it by 5 and ended up with 45. What number did I start with?
- If I multiply 6 by a number and my answer is 30, what number did I multiply by?

Next steps

Support: During oral and mental starter activities, give regular opportunities for the children to practise counting in steps of 2, 5 and 10, using their fingers to keep track. See also Year 2 Block B Unit 2.
Extension: Encourage the children to learn the division facts to go with their multiplication tables. Ask questions such as: *What do I multiply 7 by to get 14?* See also Year 2 Block B Unit 3.

Activity 7

Prior learning

Children can find halves of shapes by folding. They can find halves and quarters of a group of objects. They can sort numbers into those that can be halved exactly and those that can't.

Framework objective

Find one half, one quarter and three quarters of shapes and sets of objects

Vocabulary

fraction, part, equal parts, one whole, parts of a whole, number of parts, half, left over, fraction, one half, one quarter, three quarters

Resources

Resource sheet: Self-assessment
Classroom resources: counters, strips of paper, fruit or plastic animals

7 Which fraction?

Ask the children to write the fractions ½, ¼ and ¾ and to explain to you what each fraction means. Place some counters on the table and ask them to find different fractions (for example, quarter of 12, three quarters of 16). As they answer, they should describe their method. Repeat but without providing counters. Assess whether children can use mental methods only or need to make jottings as support. Question them to see if they understand halving and halving again to finding a quarter. Decide whether to use the self-assessment sheet for children to record their achievements and what they need to do next.

Teacher support

Less confident learners: Focus on numbers of counters up to 20. Make specific links to work the children have done on doubling and halving numbers.
More confident learners: Ask these children to find halves and quarters of numbers to 100.

Common misconception

Children do not understand the relationship between half and a quarter.
Give children a strip of paper each and ask them to fold it in half, and open it to see two parts. Then ask them to fold it in half again. They open it up to find four parts: quarters. Ask them to identify how many quarters are in one half. Extend this to seeing that if they halve a number and halve a number again, then they have found a quarter of the original number – for example, quarter of 20 is 'half 20 then half 10'.

Probing questions

- How could you find a quarter of a piece of string?
- If I have 12 pens, how could I work out how many a quarter of them would be?
- Eight squares make up this shape. How many would I need to colour to shade three quarters of the shape?

Next steps

Support: Keep the work very practical. The children need to manipulate equipment and visualise drawings. Give them apparatus (such as real fruit or plastic animals), and a context in which they need to find halves and quarters. See also Year 1 Block E Unit 2.
Extension: Provide the children with opportunities to explore other fractions such as eighths, and to find how many of these are equivalent to one half, one quarter and three quarters. See also Year 2 Block E Unit 3.

Unit 3 Securing number facts, relationships and calculating

Introduction

In this unit, children understand and use arrays to represent repeated addition and multiplication. They derive and learn to recall multiplication and division facts for the 2-, 5- and 10-times tables. They can use these facts to find the missing number in missing number sentences. They can find doubles of numbers to 20 and their corresponding halves. They can find halves and quarters of groups of objects including three-quarters. They solve problems involving multiplication and division and check their answers to see if they make sense. Threaded throughout the block are elements of the 'Using and applying' objectives.

Framework objectives	Assessment focuses		Success criteria for Year 2	Learning outcomes
	Level 2	Level 1		
(1) How much is it?				
Identify and record the information or calculation needed to solve a puzzle or problem; carry out the steps or calculations and check the solution in the context of the problem	• select the mathematics they use in some classroom activities, e.g. with support • find a starting point, identifying key facts/relevant information • use apparatus, diagrams, role-play etc to represent and clarify a problem • move between different representations of a problem e.g. a situation described in words, a diagram etc • adopt a suggested model or systematic approach • make connections and apply their knowledge to similar situations • use mathematical content from levels 1 and 2 to solve problems and investigate • begin to represent their work using symbols and simple diagrams, e.g. with support • use pictures, diagrams and symbols to communicate their thinking, or demonstrate a solution or process • begin to appreciate the need to record and develop their own methods of recording	• use mathematics as an integral part of classroom activities, e.g. with support • engage with practical mathematical activities involving sorting, counting and measuring by direct comparison • begin to understand the relevance of mathematical ideas to everyday situations by using them in role-play • represent their work with objects or pictures	• can solve problems involving multiplication and division by grouping and sharing within the context of money and number • can use practical equipment, drawings or diagrams and informal written methods to find and describe solutions • can record the necessary calculations	*When I have worked out the answer to a problem I can look again at the problem and check that the answer makes sense.*

BLOCK E

Framework objectives	Assessment focuses: Level 2	Assessment focuses: Level 1	Success criteria for Year 2	Learning outcomes
(2) Number line problems				
Present solutions to puzzles and problems in an organised way; explain decisions, methods and results in pictorial, spoken or written form, using mathematical language and number sentences	• discuss their work using mathematical language, e.g. with support • describe the strategies and methods they use in their work • engage with others' explanations, compare... evaluate... • begin to represent their work using symbols and simple diagrams, e.g. with support • use pictures, diagrams and symbols to communicate their thinking, or demonstrate a solution or process • begin to appreciate the need to record and develop their own methods of recording	• discuss their work, e.g. with support • respond to questions and ideas from peers and adults • refer to the materials they have used and talk about what they have done, patterns they have noticed etc • represent their work with objects or pictures	• can solve problems involving multiplication and division • can use practical and informal written methods to find solutions • can find the information needed to solve a problem and explain what to do in words • can write number sentences to describe what they do	*I can explain how I worked out the answer to a problem and can show my working.*
(3) Array! Array!				
Represent repeated addition and arrays as multiplication, and sharing and repeated subtraction (grouping) as division; use practical and informal written methods and related vocabulary to support multiplication and division, including calculations with remainders	• choose the appropriate operation when solving addition and subtraction problems • use repeated addition to solve multiplication problems • begin to use repeated subtraction or sharing equally to solve division problems • record their work in writing, e.g. • record their mental calculations as number sentences	• record their work, e.g. • record their work with objects, pictures or diagrams	• can relate division to multiplication • can use their knowledge of multiplication and division facts to answer simple word problems • can use sharing to answer division questions • can tell multiplication and division stories to accompany calculations	*I can use arrays to help me work out multiplication.* *I can do multiplication and division in different ways and show how I do them.*
(4) More missing numbers				
Use the symbols +, -, ×, ÷ and = to record and interpret number sentences involving all four operations; calculate the value of an unknown in a number sentence (e.g. □ ÷ 2 = 6, 30 - □ = 24)	• understand halving as a way of 'undoing' doubling and vice versa • record their work in writing, e.g. • record their mental calculations as number sentences	• record their work, e.g. • record their work with objects, pictures or diagrams • begin to use the symbols + and = to record additions	• can write number sentences for multiplication and division • can explain what each one means • can work out the missing number in calculations	*I can work out the missing numbers in number sentences.* *When I think I have the answer, I can put it in the number sentence and check whether it is correct.*

BLOCK E

Unit 3 Securing number facts, relationships and calculating

Framework objectives	Assessment focuses Level 2	Assessment focuses Level 1	Success criteria for Year 2	Learning outcomes
5 At the double!				
Understand that halving is the inverse of doubling and derive and recall doubles of all numbers to 20, and the corresponding halves	• understand halving as a way of 'undoing' doubling and vice versa • use mental calculation strategies to solve number problems including those involving money and measures, e.g. • recall doubles to 10 + 10 and other significant doubles, e.g. double 50p is 100p or £1 • begin to use halves and quarters, e.g. • work out halves of numbers up to 20 and begin to recall them	• begin to know some addition facts, e.g. • doubles of numbers to double 5	• can double all numbers to 10 and find the related halves • can record calculations using '× 2' and '÷ 2' • can use these facts to find doubles and halves of numbers to 20 • can use these skills to double and halve amounts of money practically	*I can double all numbers up to 20 and can find the matching halves.*
6 Table facts				
Derive and recall multiplication facts for the 2-, 5- and 10-times tables and the related division facts; recognise multiples of 2, 5 and 10	• recognise sequences of numbers, including odd and even numbers, e.g. • continue a sequence that increases or decreases in regular steps • recognise numbers from counting in tens or twos • choose the appropriate operation when solving addition or subtraction problems • use repeated addition to solve multiplication problems • begin to use repeated subtraction or sharing equally to solve division problems	• order numbers to 10 • begin to count in twos	• can use multiplication and division facts for the 2-, 5- and 10-times tables by counting in twos, fives and tens • can use practical apparatus, counting or drawing to support them • can use patterns and relationships to work these out (for example, 2-times table numbers end with an even digit, 5-times with a 5 or zero and 10-times with zero)	*I know my 2-, 5- and 10-times tables.* *I can work out divisions that go with the tables.*
7 What fraction is it?				
Find one half, one quarter and three quarters of shapes and sets of objects	• begin to use halves and quarters, e.g. • use the concept of a fraction of a small quantity in a practical context such as sharing sweets between two and getting half each, among four and getting a quarter each • work out halves of numbers to 20 and begin to recall them • relate the concept of half of a small quantity to the concept of half of a shape, e.g. • shade one half or one quarter of a given shape, including shapes divided into equal regions	• begin to use the fraction one half, e.g. • halve shapes, including folding paper shapes, lengths of string • put water in a clear container so that it is about 'half full' • halve an even number of objects	• can recognise and write ½ and ¼ • can fold shapes into half and then in half again to make quarters • know that four quarters make a whole and that each quarter must be the same size • can find half or set of objects and know that finding half of a number is the same as dividing it by 2 • can find a quarter of a set of objects by sharing them equally among four	*I can find three-quarters of a set of objects or of a shape.*

BLOCK E

Activity 1

Prior learning
Children can solve problems involving multiplication or division by grouping and sharing within the context of money and number. They can tell division and multiplication stories.

Framework objective
Identify and record the information or calculation needed to solve a puzzle or problem; carry out the steps or calculations and check the solution in the context of the problem

Vocabulary
problem, solve, calculate, calculation, inverse, answer, method, explain, predict, pattern, order

Resources
Interactive activity: How much is it?
Resource sheet: Self-assessment
Classroom resources: bananas, 1p, 2p, 5p and 10p coins

1 How much is it?

Work with a group. Show some real bananas and say that each costs 15p. *I want to buy two bananas. How much will that cost?* Show the interactive activity 'How much is it?' and ask the children to show the cost using the fewest coins possible. Discuss their methods. Now extend the problem: *I want to buy four bananas. How much will that be?* Observe the children's methods: do they partition 15 and find 4 × 10p and 4 × 5p and total their results; do they double the cost of two bananas; do they use a different method? Encourage them to check their answers. Decide whether to use the self-assessment sheet for children to record their achievements and what they need to do next.

Teacher support
Less confident learners: Work on the same problem but with one banana priced at 10p.
More confident learners: Change the price of the bananas to 25p each. Encourage the children to check their answers by using the inverse operation.

Common misconceptions
Children do not understand how to work through a problem.
Take children through the problem step by step. First ask them to find the question, next the numerical information and finally to work out what they need to do. Scribe for them as appropriate.

Children do not recognise the value of different coins.
Give the children some pennies each. Ask them to count out 10 pennies and exchange them for a 10p coin. Repeat for 5p and 2p coins. Then encourage children to find the total by adding 5p to the 10p and then the 2p.

Probing questions
- There are 15 sweets in a bag. How many will there be in two identical bags?
- How did you work that out? How do know if you are right?
- If each sweet costs 5p, how much will eight sweets cost?

Next steps
Support: Say: *One banana costs 10p.* Give the children 10p coins and ask them to use coins to show you how much three bananas would cost. Then, together, count in tens to 30p pointing at each 10p coin as you do so. Repeat this for other numbers of bananas. See also Year 2 Block B Unit 2.
Extension: Challenge the children to solve the problem for different banana prices (for example, one banana costs 18p). Encourage them to use appropriate strategies and explain their methods. See also Year 3 Block B Unit 1.

Activity 2

Prior learning

Children can solve problems involving multiplication or division. They can find the information needed to explain and solve a problem. They can write number sentences to show their method.

Framework objective

Present solutions to puzzles and problems in an organised way; explain decisions, methods and results in pictorial, spoken or written form, using mathematical language and number sentences

Vocabulary

problem, solve, calculate, calculation, inverse, answer, method, explain, predict, pattern, order

Resources

Interactive activity: Number line problems
Resource sheets: 0-100 number lines, 0-30 number lines, Self-assessment

2 Number line problems

Work with a small group. Display the interactive activity 'Number line problems'. Pose this problem: *Charlie had three pots of pens on his table. Each pot had seven pens in it. How many pens were there altogether?* Ask the children to consider how to solve the problem, what information they have and how to use it. Encourage them to use their number lines. Invite someone to explain their method by demonstrating on the on-screen number line. Invite someone else to explain how they could check the answer using a number line. Repeat for similar problems. Decide whether to use the self-assessment sheet for children to record their achievements and what they need to do next.

Teacher support

Less confident learners: Concentrate on multiplying amounts by 2.
More confident learners: Pose problems that involve multiplying by 3, 4 or 6.

Common misconceptions

Children cannot identify what to do when tackling a word problem.
Rephrase the problem or revisit the vocabulary used. Set out the problem with practical equipment and, as you say the problem, touch and move the equipment as appropriate.

Children cannot use the number line to demonstrate their thinking.
Provide a 0-30 number line and help children count on in ones, then twos, then threes, making the necessary jumps.

Probing questions

- Can you make up a problem that uses this calculation: 3 × 4?
- Penny worked out that 25 ÷ 5 = 5. How could she have worked this out?
- I am thinking of a number and multiply it by 3. My answer is 21. How can you find my number?

Next steps

Support: Give regular opportunities for the children to explain how they solved a problem by using a number line. Encourage them to begin to draw their own number lines and to make forward and backward jumps as appropriate. See also Year 2 Block A Unit 3.
Extension: Pose two-step problems such as: *Charlie had three pots on his table. Each contained eight pens. He gave seven pens to a friend. How many did he have left?* Encourage the children to explain each stage of the problem, modelling their explanation on a number line. See also Year 3 Block B Unit 1.

Activity 3

Prior learning

Children can relate division to multiplication. They can use their knowledge of multiplication and division facts to answer simple word problems. They can tell multiplication and division stories to accompany calculations.

Framework objective

Represent repeated addition and arrays as multiplication, and sharing and repeated subtraction (grouping) as division; use practical and informal written methods and related vocabulary to support multiplication and division, including calculations with remainders

Vocabulary

count on, count back, lots of, groups of, equal groups of, grouping, array, row, column, multiply, multiplication, multiplied by (×), multiple, share, divide, division, divided by (÷), remainder, round up, round down, double, halve

Resources

Interactive activity: Array! Array!
Resource sheet: Self-assessment
Classroom resources: whiteboards and pens, £1 coins, counters

3 Array! Array!

Reveal the interactive activity 'Array! Array!' to the whole class. Write some calculations (for example, 5 × 4), and ask the children to tell you what the repeated addition would be. (5 + 5 + 5 + 5.) Ask those children you particularly wish to assess to come to the front to show jumps along the number line to show this and to find the answer. Ask them to check by jumping back and also by drawing an array on their whiteboards. Repeat for other one-digit numbers multiplied by 2, 5 or 10. Decide whether to use the self-assessment sheet.

Teacher support

Less confident learners: Ask these children to draw arrays for calculations such as 2 × 4, 5 × 3 and 10 × 3. They should also identify and write the corresponding repeated addition number sentences.
More confident learners: Ask the children to identify the two repeated addition number sentences for an array.

Common misconception

Children do not understand that repeated addition and multiplication are equivalent.
Give children ten £1 coins each and ask them to group them in twos. Agree that £2 + £2 + £2 + £2 + £2 are £10 and that this can be thought of as five lots of £2. Draw a number line and, starting at zero, count on five jumps of 2. Repeat for other repeated additions and equivalent related multiplications.

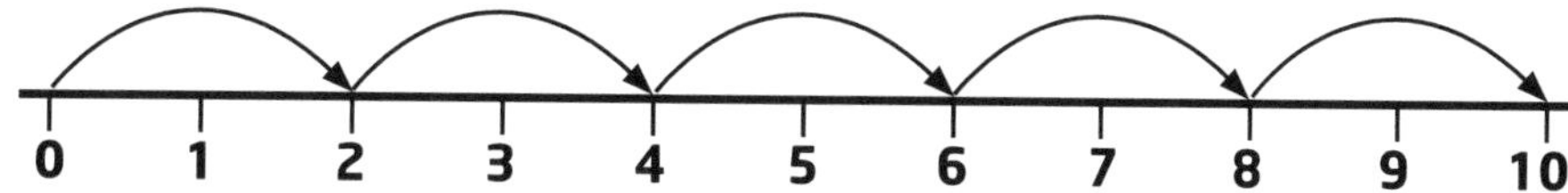

Probing questions

- How could you arrange 15 counters in equal rows?
- What would this look like as a multiplication number sentence?

Next steps

Support: Give the children 12 counters and ask them to set them out in equal rows and write the repeated addition number sentences. Ask them how they could arrange the counters in a different way. See also Year 2 Block E Unit 2.
Extension: Encourage the children to think of all the different arrays they could make with 24 counters. See also Year 3 Block E Unit 1.

BLOCK E

Activity 4

Prior learning
Children can write number sentences for multiplication and division. They can explain what each one means. They are able to work out the missing number in such calculations.

Framework objective
Use the symbols +, –, ×, ÷ and = to record and interpret number sentences involving all four operations; calculate the value of an unknown in a number sentence (e.g. □ ÷ 2 = 6, 30 - □ = 24)

Vocabulary
place value, partition, ones, tens, hundreds, single-digit number, two-digit number, add, subtract, plus (+), minus (–), sign, equals (=), operation, symbol, number sentence, number line

Resources
Display page: More missing numbers
Resource sheet: Self-assessment
Classroom resources: counters

4 More missing numbers

Reveal the display page 'More missing numbers'. Ask the children to find the missing numbers as quickly as they can and to use their own methods to check their answers. Ask individuals to explain what they did. Next, write these missing number sentences on the board: □ × ◊ = 20 and □ ÷ ◊ = 2. Ask the children to write as many possible answers as they can. Sit with the group you wish to assess and observe how they do this. Decide whether to use the self-assessment sheet for children to record their achievements and next steps.

Teacher support
Less confident learners: Focus on □ × ◊ = 20, providing number lines and practical equipment to help children find different ways to make 20.
More confident learners: Give these children answers such as 36 and 4 and ask them to find multiplication and division facts that use them in times tables other than those of 2, 5 and 10.

Common misconceptions
Children do not realise that repeated addition and multiplication are equivalent.
Provide counters and ask children to group ten of them in groups of two. Explain that 2 + 2 + 2 + 2 + 2 is 10, which is five lots of 2. Count 5 two times using fingers to show 5 × 2 is the same. Repeat for other multiplication facts.

Children do not realise that repeated subtraction and division are equivalent.
Provide ten counters and ask children to subtract lots of two. Write 10 - 2 - 2 - 2 - 2 - 2 = 0. Ask children how many lots of two they have subtracted. Explain that this is the same as writing 10 ÷ 2 = 5. Repeat for other division facts.

Probing questions
- I am thinking of a number. I divide it by 5 and my answer is 4. What was my number?
- I am thinking of a number. I multiply it by 6 and my answer is 30. What was my number? How can you record this?

Next steps
Support: Ask the children to make arrays to show possible solutions to missing-number sentences such as: 12 ÷ □ = 6. They arrange 12 counters in six equal groups and then count to see how many are in each. See also Year 2 Block E Unit 2.
Extension: Challenge the children to make up missing number problems that involve multiplying and dividing by 3 or 4. See also Year 3 Block B Unit 1.

Activity 5

Prior learning

Children know the doubles and halves of numbers to 10. They can record calculations using '× 2' and '÷ 2'. They can use these facts to find doubles and halves of money and numbers to 20.

Framework objective

Understand that halving is the inverse of doubling and derive and recall doubles of all numbers to 20, and the corresponding halves

Vocabulary

doubling, halving, double, halve

Resources

Resource sheet: Self-assessment
Classroom resources: whiteboards and pens, models to illustrate a half (for example, biscuits, plastic farm animals, counters)

5 At the double!

Ask the children to write a number from 10 to 20 on their whiteboards and then to double it. Do they partition into tens and units, double each then recombine, or do they just know the answer? Invite the children to make up some word problems to ask a friend. Give examples first, such as: *Sally had 14 sweets. Tom had double that. How many sweets did Tom have? I had 32 stickers. I gave half to my friend. How many did I give my friend?* Assess the children's ability to use and apply their doubling and halving skills. Decide whether to use the self-assessment sheet for children to record their achievements and next steps.

Teacher support

Less confident learners: Remind the children about partitioning numbers greater than 10 (for example, 13 = 10 + 3). To double such a number, ask them to double each part and write the new number sentence: 20 + 6 = 26.
More confident learners: Challenge these children to find doubles of multiples of 5 and 10 to 100.

Common misconceptions

Children have little concept of what 'half' is.
Provide concrete models to illustrate a half (for example, plastic farm animals and a loop to represent a field). Tell children a farmer has six horses and wants to put half of them in the field. Focus on halves being two equal amounts.

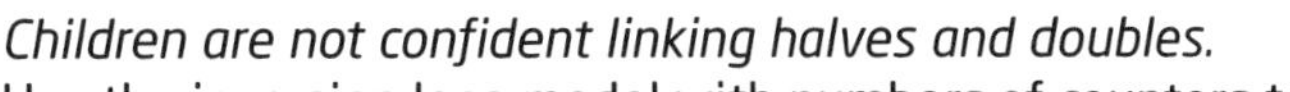

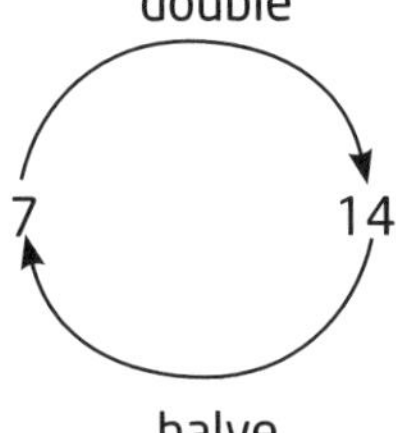

Children are not confident linking halves and doubles.
Use the inversion loop model with numbers of counters to illustrate.

Probing questions

- I am thinking of a number. I double it and add 2. My answer is 12. What number did I double?
- How did you work that out?
- There are 26 children in the class. Half of them are boys. How many girls are there?

Next steps

Support: Use more partitioning. For example, for double 15, write 15 = 10 + 5, then double 10 and 5 to give 20 + 10 = 30. See also Year 2 Block E Unit 2.
Extension: Challenge the children to make up some 'I am thinking of a number' questions to ask a friend. Encourage them to add or take away a number at the end: *I am thinking of a number. I double it and take away 3. I now have 15. What was my number?* See also Year 3 Block D Unit 1.

Activity 6

Prior learning

Children can use multiplication and division facts for the 2-, 5- and 10-times tables using practical apparatus, counting, patterns or drawing as support.

Framework objective

Derive and recall multiplication facts for the 2-, 5- and 10-times tables and the related division facts; recognise multiples of 2, 5 and 10

Vocabulary

multiply, multiplication, multiplied by (×), multiple, share equally, divide, division, divided by (÷)

Resources

Resource sheet: Self-assessment
Classroom resources: whiteboards and pens

6 Table facts

Ask the children for multiplication and division facts. For example: *5 × 6 = ? What is double 7? How many tens make 80?* Write some missing-number sentences that use these facts on the board for the children to complete, such as 18 ÷ □ = 9, □ × 10 = 50. Observe the children you particularly wish to assess to see how confidently they answer and the strategies they use. Do they recall the times-table facts, do they need to make drawings or do they use their fingers? Decide whether to use the self-assessment sheet for children to record their achievements and what they need to do next.

Teacher support

Less confident learners: Focus on asking the children basic times-tables facts, such as 5 × 7, 2 × 8.
More confident learners: Rather than simply asking for times-tables facts, ask questions that require the children to use this knowledge to find the answers. For example: *How many sixes make 30?*

Common misconception

Children cannot recall times-tables facts.
Provide children with cards that show multiplication facts. they should hold up the appropriate fact to answer your question. Encourage children to refer to these cards when answering word problems involving multiplication so that they practise problem-solving skills while learning their times tables.

Probing questions

- Five times four is the same as ten times what?
- Which of these numbers appear in the 5-times table: 12, 10, 35, 48, 50?
- Which appear in the 2-times table? How do you know?

Next steps

Support: Give regular opportunities for the children to practise counting in twos, fives and tens and to link this with the times-tables facts. See also Year 2 Block E Unit 2.
Extension: Encourage the children to work with a partner to ask each other times-table facts for multiplication and division. They could time each other to see how fast they can recall them. See also Year 3 Block D Unit 1.

Activity 7

Prior learning
Children can recognise and write ½ and ¼. They fold shapes into half and then in half again to make quarters. They know that four quarters make a whole and that finding half of a number is the same as dividing it by 2.

Framework objective
Find one half, one quarter and three quarters of shapes and sets of objects

Vocabulary
fraction, part, equal parts, one whole, parts of a whole, number of parts, half, left over, fraction, one half, one quarter, three quarters

Resources
Interactive activity: What fraction is it?
Classroom resources: strips of paper, counters or countable objects (such as pencils), coins

7 What fraction is it?

Open the interactive activity 'What fraction is it?'. Drag eight 10p coins to the working area, and ask the children to write how much half the amount will be. *What is one quarter? What is three quarters?* Invite the children to draw a loop around half of the coins, a quarter of them and another around three quarters of them. Repeat for other amounts that can be halved and quartered. Drag six 10p coins to the working area. Ask the children to find half (3 × 10p), then to tell you how to find a quarter: halve 2 × 10p, and then halve the remaining 10p (2 × 5p) to make 5p, so a quarter is 15p.

Teacher support
Less confident learners: Concentrate on finding halves and quarters of amounts made up of 1p, 5p and 10p coins.
More confident learners: Give these children opportunities to find halves and quarters of amounts given in large-value coins (for example, half and then quarter of 20p).

Common misconception
Children do not understand the relationship between half and a quarter.
Give each child a strip of paper and ask them to fold in half. Ask them to open it to see two parts. Then ask them to fold it in half again. They open it up to find four parts: quarters. Ask them to identify how many quarters are in one half. They should be able to see that there are two quarters in each half.

Probing questions
- How many quarters are the same as a half? How can you prove that?
- I had 24 counters and put three quarters of them in a pot. How many did I put in the pot?
- How can you record that?

Next steps
Support: Give the children plenty of practical experience in finding halves, quarters and three quarters of counters, pencils or something similar. Pose simple problems in real-life contexts for them to answer. See also Year 2 Block E Unit 2.
Extension: Ask the children to find halves, quarters and three quarters of amounts of money. For example, give them one 50p coin, three 10p coins and four pennies (84p). Observe how they find one half, one quarter and three quarters. See also Year 3 Block D Unit 1.

BLOCK E

Units 1, 2 & 3 Periodic assessment

These activities can be used at the end of this block to assess those children that you think have achieved the objectives.

What's the number?

Framework objective
Use the symbols +, –, ×, ÷ and = to record and interpret number sentences involving all four operations; calculate the value of an unknown in a number sentence (for example, □ ÷ 2 = 6, 30 - □ = 24)

Learning outcomes

- I know how to write number sentences for multiplication and division as well as addition and subtraction.
- I can explain what my number sentence means.
- I know how to write number sentences for multiplication and for division.
- I can explain what different numbers sentences mean.
- I can work out the missing numbers in number sentences.
- I can put an answer in a number sentence to check whether it is correct.

1. Write on the board: ○ × □ = 20. Ask the children to write at least two different number sentences (such as 2 × 10 = 20 and 10 × 2 = 20). Expect some children also to write 4 × 5 = 20 and 5 × 4 = 20. Now write ○ ÷ □ = 5 on the board. Give the children one minute to write as many as calculations as they can. Repeat for other numbers from the 2-, 5- and 10-times tables.

2. The aim of this assessment activity is for the children to show that they understand the numerical information within a word problem and the operation needed to find the answer to a multiplication or division problem. Pose some simple word problems, such as: *Tim has 25 toy dinosaurs. He puts them into groups of five. How many groups does he have?* Encourage the children to jot down the information before making up the number sentence.

3. Write some missing-number sentences on the board, such as □ × 2 = 14, 25 ÷ □ = 5, 37 ÷ □ = 7 remainder 2. Ask the children to write the complete number sentence on their whiteboards. Next, move on to questions that are more open-ended, such as ○ × □ = 18. Observe how the children answer these. Encourage them to think of more than just the times-table facts they have been working with, such as 9 × 2 = 18, 6 × 3 = 18. Finally, write the following open number sentences on the board: ○ × □ = △ and ○ ÷ □ = △. Give the children one minute to make up as many different number sentences as they can. Decide whether to use the self-assessment sheet for children to record their achievements and next steps.

Face the facts

Framework objective
Derive and recall multiplication facts for the 2-, 5- and 10-times tables and the related division facts; recognise multiples of 2, 5 and 10

Learning outcomes

- I can recognise some of the 2-, 5- and 10-times tables and can explain the patterns I see.
- I can use these patterns to see if other numbers belong to the sequence.
- I know some of my times tables for 2, 5 and 10.
- I can use counting or other strategies for those I don't know.
- I know that multiples of 5 end in 5 or zero.
- I can work out divisions that go with the times-table facts.

Provide each child with a copy of the worksheet 'Face the facts'. Remind them of how a multiplication grid works, and ask them to complete both the grids. Sit with the children you particularly wish to assess and observe whether they can recall the times-tables facts easily.

Name Date

Face the facts

- Complete the multiplication grid.

×	2	5	10
2			
4			
1			
5			

- Complete the multiplication grid.

×	2	5	10
7			
6			
3			
8			

How easy?

Red
Amber
Green

How do you think you have done?

Transitional assessment

Activity	Type	Level	Description
1.1	Single-level written assessment	1	20-minute formal test paper covering objectives from all Strands of the Framework at Level 1
1.2	Single-level written assessment	1	20-minute formal test paper covering objectives from all Strands of the Framework at Level 1
1.3	Single-level written assessment	1	20-minute formal test paper covering objectives from all Strands of the Framework at Level 1
1.4	Single-level oral and practical assessment	1	Oral paper administered to groups of up to four children, covering objectives from all Strands of the Framework at Level 1
1.5	Single-level oral and practical assessment	1	Oral paper administered to groups of up to four children, covering objectives from all Strands of the Framework at Level 1
2.1	Single-level written assessment	2	30-minute formal test paper covering objectives from all Strands of the Framework at Level 2
2.2	Single-level written assessment	2	30-minute formal test paper covering objectives from all Strands of the Framework at Level 2
2.3	Single-level written assessment	2	30-minute formal test paper covering objectives from all Strands of the Framework at Level 2
2.4	Single-level oral assessment	2	Approximately 5-minute oral paper covering objectives from all Strands of the Framework at Level 2
2.5	Single-level oral assessment	2	Approximately 5-minute oral paper covering objectives from all Strands of the Framework at Level 2
3.1a 3.1b	Single-level written assessments	3	Two 20-minute formal test papers covering objectives from all Strands of the Framework at Level 3 (one calculator, one non-calculator)
3.2a 3.2b	Single-level written assessments	3	Two 20-minute formal test papers covering objectives from all Strands of the Framework at Level 3 (one calculator, one non-calculator)
3.3a 3.3b	Single-level written assessments	3	Two 20-minute formal test papers covering objectives from all Strands of the Framework at Level 3 (one calculator, one non-calculator)
3.4	Single-level oral assessment	3	Approximately 5-minute oral paper covering objectives from all Strands of the Framework at Level 3
3.5	Single-level oral assessment	3	Approximately 5-minute oral paper covering objectives from all Strands of the Framework at Level 3

Written test instructions

Allow 20 minutes for each paper at Levels 1 and 3, and 30 minutes for each paper at Level 2.

Children should work so that they cannot see each other's work.
Do not explain questions or read numbers to the children.
For Level 1, teachers should read the questions aloud to the children. For Levels 2 and 3, they may choose to read the questions aloud if they feel it is appropriate. The test may be administered to groups of children or to the whole class. The total marks available for each paper are given in the mark scheme.

Say to the children:

Here are some questions (I am going to read some questions) for you to answer.
For some questions you will write your answer in a box. [Show example.]
For some questions you may need to draw lines or rings to show your answer. [Show example.]
If you make a mistake, you should cross it out (or rub it out neatly) and write your answer clearly.
You may use spaces on the paper to do any working out that may help you.
Try to work out the answer to each question before going on to the next one.
If you can't answer a question, move on to the next one – it may be easier.

Equipment for each child

Level 1: pencil, eraser (or children may cross out mistakes), interlocking cubes
Levels 2 and 3: pencil, eraser (or children may cross out mistakes), a 30cm ruler (marked in millimetres), structured apparatus consisting of tens and units (for example, base 10 equipment, interlocking cubes), mirror, tracing paper

Oral test instructions

Level 1: This oral and practical assessment can be administered to groups of up to four children. Read the questions to the children. Allow sufficient time for a child to work out an answer. Children respond orally. 1 mark per question: 10 marks total. Separate teacher resources are listed for each paper.
Levels 2 and 3: Read questions to the children no more than twice. Allow five seconds for each answer. Children record their answers on paper (necessary equipment: pencil, eraser (or children may cross out mistakes), 30cm ruler). 1 mark per question: 15 marks total. Separate teacher resources are listed for each paper.

Levelling the children

Add together the marks from an oral test and a written test.

Level 1		Level 2		Level 3	
Below Level 1	0 - 10 marks	Below Level 2	0 - 15 marks	Below Level 3	0 - 21 marks
Low Level 1	11 - 14 marks	Low Level 2	16 - 22 marks	Low Level 3	22 - 31 marks
Secure Level 1	15 - 19 marks	Secure Level 2	22 - 28 marks	Secure Level 3	32 - 40 marks
High Level 1	20 - 24 marks	High Level 2	28 - 36 marks	High Level 3	40 - 50 marks

When awarding an end-of-year Teacher Assessment Level, teachers also need to consider a child's performance on Periodic and Day-to-Day Assessments.

TRANSITIONAL

Mathematics: making a level judgement

Use these steps to formalise your assessments of pupils' mathematics into level judgements.

You will need

- evidence of the pupil's mathematics that shows most independence, for example from work in other subjects as well as in mathematics lessons
- other evidence about the pupil as a mathematician, for example notes on plans, the pupil's own reflections, your own recollections of classroom interactions, oral answers given during mental starters
- a copy of the assessment guidelines for the level borderline that is your starting point.

Step 1: Making best-fit judgements

Within each assessment focus, draw on the pupil's work and other evidence including what you know about the pupil's mathematics. Use the criteria in the assessment guidelines to decide which level provides the best fit.

Step 2: Work through Ma2 Number

Begin with the assessment guidelines for Ma2 Number.

Look at the criteria within each AF. Decide which level describes the pupil best.

Record the level for each AF in the appropriate box.

Record 'insufficient evidence' (IE) if you do not know enough about this aspect of the pupil's mathematics to make a judgement. This has implications for planning.

If you feel the pupil is operating below the level, check the criteria on the assessment guidelines for the level below.

Step 3: Making an overall level judgement for Ma2 Number

Now make your level decision for Ma2 Number.

- Your AF judgements give an impression of the best-fit level for Ma2.
- Read the complete level descriptions for both levels to confirm your impression of the best-fit level for Ma2

Decide whether the level is Low, Secure or High. Do this by thinking about what the pupil demonstrates:

- how much of the level
- how consistently
- how independently
- in what range of contexts.

Tick the relevant Low, Secure or High box for the level.

Step 4: Repeat the process for Ma3, Ma4 and then Ma1

For the Ma1 judgement, consider how the pupil uses and applies the mathematics of Ma2, Ma3 and Ma4.

APP

Name Date

Activity name ______________________________

Objective:
Learning outcome:
Comments:

Self-assessment

How well did you do this? ______________________________

____

____

____

What do you still need to do? ______________________________

____

____

____

How easy?

How do you think you have done?

____

____